Implementing *Quality* Through BS5750 (ISO 9000)

PETER JACKSON

and

DAVID ASHTON

KOGAN
PAGE

First published in 1993
Reprinted 1993 (twice)

Kogan Page Limited
120 Pentonville Road
London N1 9JN

British Library Cataloguing in Publication Data

A CIP record for this book is available from the British Library.

ISBN 0 7494 0797 2

Typeset by Saxon Graphics Ltd, Derby
Printed and bound in Great Britain by Biddles Ltd, Guildford and King's Lynn

CONTENTS

To the memory of
Stanley Gordon Ashton
1927-1992

PREFACE

This book originated in the two authors working together to implement BS 5750. One (Peter Jackson) is a manager of a service company which in 1991 had decided to seek registration for BS 5750 in a field where no other company had preceded it. The other author (Dave Ashton) worked as a consultant and advised the Company on how to successfully implement a quality system to meet BS 5750. As a spin-off from their work together, both believed that there was a need for a practical guide to BS 5750.

This book is the result. It has been written to meet the needs of owners and managers of smaller companies – perhaps up to a hundred employees and rather more in labour-intensive businesses. No prior knowledge or experience of formal quality assurance is assumed. The needs of both manufacturers and service providers are covered – one author has spent his working life in service activities, while the other came into quality management through production engineering.

While the primary aim has been to produce a practical guide to BS 5750 implementation, some understanding of the underlying principles is necessary and this is covered in Part One. Part Two provides, in some detail, the practical guidance and includes specimen material which should be adaptable to many different businesses.

Purely for reasons of convenience, 'he' and other forms of the masculine gender are used throughout. There just is no satisfactory neutral form and 'he or she' etc always seems clumsy. There is, of course, absolutely no reason why women should not be the prime movers in instigating and managing quality systems.

Finally, the authors thank their respective employers – Business & Market Research and Daisley Associates – not only for allowing the direct or indirect use of material but also for tolerating some distraction from day-to-day work.

Peter Jackson
Dave Ashton
September 1992

THE PRINCIPLES

The purpose of this book is to provide a practical guide for an organisation seeking BS 5750. However, some underlying principles of BS 5750 and quality systems generally need to be understood before any plans are made. Chapters 1 and 2 cover this essential background.

With an understanding of BS 5750, the reader must decide whether it meets the needs of his own organisation. Both benefits and drawbacks are considered, as is the relevance of BS 5750 – for which types of organisation is the Standard appropriate? The important topic of cost is also covered in chapter 3.

Part One concludes, in chapter 4, with an overview of implementation. What are the steps to BS 5750. The details are the subject of Part Two: an action plan to achieve BS 5750.

1 QUALITY – WHAT IT IS AND HOW TO GET IT

This is specifically a book about BS 5750 rather than quality in general. However, since BS 5750 is a standard for quality we need in this first chapter to understand what quality means in a business environment and how it can be achieved.

QUALITY AND EXCELLENCE

In common usage, the concept of quality is linked to excellence; achieving the best or being at the forefront:

- We shall strive for quality.
- This company is at the quality end of the market.
- He is a man of quality.
- This product is pure quality.

In this sense quality is an absolute and either very difficult to achieve or the province of a select few.

Of course, this sense of quality is a vital part of our culture and will remain so. But as a practical concept to help us run our businesses it is a hindrance. Quality in the sense of the best/excellence leads nowhere; it really does not help us to run our company better. Consider common statements such as:

- We only wish we could concentrate on quality goods, but we cannot afford to do this. We would price ourselves out of the market.
- We operate in a commodity market. Everyone's product is the same and quality just does not come into it.

We are being told that quality is either not affordable or not needed.

The story below further illustrates the limitations of a quality concept based on the best/excellence.

Successful Defects

A bright new shopping centre is clearly struggling. Because of a general business downturn or for other reasons, the anticipated store traffic has not yet materialised. There is one exception; a reject pottery shop selling 'seconds', famous brand pots at half price or less. Alone in the mall this store is clearly thriving.

The pottery manufacturer whose brands make up the stock of the seconds shop is not prospering either. The only part of the output where demand exceeds supply is its rejects (which are, however, plentiful because of the factory's high product quality standards). The managing director is bitter: 'This Company has been committed to the highest quality for a hundred years but where is it leading us to? Bankruptcy. The punters don't want quality they just look for bargains. Any old thing which will hold their tea. Never mind if the colour's off and the shape's out as long as it is half-price. The only thing I can see is to increase our reject rate and sell most of our pots as "seconds".'

The paradox in this story is that the pursuit of quality seems a failure. The shop's customers will overlook many of the product characteristics which the manufacturer believes makes his pots so excellent, provided the price is low enough. Also, the one shop in the mall which aggressively eschews a 'quality image', alone prospers with a classic 'pile them high' display. Back at the pottery, the quality standards, so rigorously enforced, lead to mounting stocks of unsold goods, but a booming demand for the rejects. All this reflects some major business issues, but the paradoxes themselves are the result of a failure in understanding. A practical and effective concept of quality resolves a semantic confusion and may point to some effective business strategies to overcome some of the problems.

ANOTHER VIEW OF QUALITY

Another view of quality avoids the trap of an unattainable excellence and focuses on the needs of a group on which every business entirely depends – the customer. Another story to help change our frame of reference:

A Tale Of Two Watches

Hubert and Rod are having a beer after work. It is getting time to go home and Hubert is looking at his watch (with a heavy gold band, you cannot miss it).

'That's a smart watch, Hubert.'

'Yes, it's a R***x. I have had it a year or two and it has never let me down. Accurate to a minute a month or something, shows the date and of course it is self-winding.'

At this point Hubert glances at Rod's own watch – a C***o.

'How can you bear to put up with a watch like that, Rod? I would be ashamed.'

Rod is not at all put out.

'Well, it may not be quite a R***x, but like yours it hasn't let me down yet. It is also accurate to a few seconds a year, you don't need to wind it either. Of course it shows the date, not to mention having an alarm, a stop-watch and if I need it I can check the time in LA. It cost me all of £10. How much was your R***x, Hubert?'

'Oh a hundred times more, but of course it will last me a lifetime.'

This left Rod still unimpressed.

'Well that's good – but no use to me. I am hopeless with things and the chances are I will lose my watch in six months. Certainly within a year. So the two–year guarantee is more than adequate for me.'

Hubert sniggered into his Mexican lager.

'As usual, Rod, you don't see it at all. This watch is making an important statement. About me, what I am and that only the best will do.'

'Well, Hubert, I hear what you are saying. Yes, I know you need all the help you can get . . .'

The point here is that both Hubert and Rod are seeking quality in their watches and both feel they are achieving it. In different ways both the £10 and the £1000 watch meet their requirements, whether these are strictly functional (accuracy), related to life expectancy or giving confidence and psychological support.

The idea of meeting requirements – which differ between customers – is the concept of quality underlying this book and BS 5750.

QUALITY AS MEETING CUSTOMERS' REQUIREMENTS

Using this definition, quality is the goal of each and every business. No company can regard quality as *not* a central concern and all can and must strive to attain it.

The concept is very simple, although there are quite a few implications to think about. Firstly there is the focus on *customers*, who are brought right where they belong – to the heart of the business. Businesses vary in every imaginable way but all depend on customers and their continuing orders. In a free market, how many businesses will keep their customers if they do not meet requirements? In the long run, none.

Customers in any market are not homogenous. They can be segmented in many ways, into smaller groups with common requirements. Quality, in the sense of meeting customer requirements, therefore entails developing a product range for a range of customer groups. In many markets a business will recognise that practically it cannot meet the requirements of all possible customers and by deliberate choice will leave some to smaller, niche suppliers. Alternatively, the business may itself choose to be highly specialised and cater for the requirements of a selected group of customers. In this case the pursuit of quality (customers' requirements) may overlap with the conventional sense of a quality (excellent) company. However, the larger suppliers focusing on the 'mass' market should be no less committed to quality (meeting requirements). In fact, they cannot be otherwise; a surviving company has to be a quality company.

Returning to the shopping mall, the 'seconds' shop and the pottery; the concept of quality in the sense of meeting requirements should point to some solutions. The shop is meeting a budget-conscious group (in a recession-hit town?) to whom minor defects can be overlooked at a low price, although it is very unlikely that these defects are actually valued. The 'pile them high' display gives the comfort of 'no frills' retailing (what the bargainhunter seeks). In all, the 'seconds' shop is succeeding in meeting its customers' requirements. What of the pottery? Here the need may be to recognise the need for a functional range of pots which can be sold at a budget price and perhaps through the regular outlets. It will almost certainly be better to reduce the supply of expensively produced rejects and direct resources to such a new range. If this strategy succeeds, customers' requirements may be even better met (with budget but perfect pots) and possibly the trade of some of the 'first line' stores in the mall will improve. The 'seconds' shop will suffer initially as customers find their requirements met in a different way, but it is likely that their innovatory retailing skills will be successfully redirected. And all this because of a new understanding of quality!

Requirements (as in 'quality as meeting requirements') need to be understood in the widest possible sense. It is not just product (or service) features in a narrow technical meaning. The case study opposite illustrates this point.

Requirements, therefore, are the totality of *all* the features of a product or service of significance to a customer. Some of these may be implicit and inherent rather than explicitly requested by the customer but are nevertheless vital. When booking a flight to New York we do not feel the need to specify that

The Best Boat Water Heater

Consultants were asked to advise a well-established manufacturer of gas water heaters designed for leisure boats. The problems, if not the cause and solution, were simple: declining sales and vanishing profits.

A limited investigation in the market confirmed the company's belief that their products were technically second to none; in this sense, excellent. Furthermore, engineering analysis proved that they were both very fuel-efficient and offered real safety features. So, in a narrow sense, the products met customer requirements. They were quality.

However, the same investigation of the market demonstrated that in other respects customers' requirements were not met.

To match cabin décor, boat-builders (the key customer group) required heaters in a range of colours. The company only offered the product in a white casing. With limited storage space, most boat-yards did not want to hold stocks of appliances, but at the critical stage the lack of a water heater could put back the final schedule. The company had recognised problems in delivery methods. Finally, whilst the technical qualities of the heaters were acknowledged, a rather cheaper if less efficient heater was thought more suitable below the luxury end of the boat market. All in all, once requirements were seen in a wider context, the cause of the company's problems and the solution became apparent.

the plane should be adequately serviced: it is an implicit requirement that the airline takes steps to minimise the chances of the wings falling off. The concept of meeting customers' requirements, therefore, also implies products and services which are *fit for purpose* – another common, practical definition of quality.

Whether the requirements are implicit or explicit, meeting them requires their identification and understanding. Again, the pursuit of quality implies that customers have a central position in the business. Unless we are close enough to understand their requirements how can we ever hope to satisfy them? In bespoke types of business this will involve discussion and agreement of the specific needs of individual customers, while in off-the-shelf businesses knowledge of requirements requires continual feedback through customer satisfaction monitoring or market research programmes, or maybe just ongoing and day-to-day contact with customers.

Meeting customer requirements is also a dynamic activity. Both customers and their needs change and the supplier must recognise this. Unless the company's own programme of innovation at least matches the pace of change among customers, requirements will cease to be met and decline will follow.

QUALITY IS AFFORDABLE

If quality is defined in terms of meeting customer requirements, then not only *must* it be affordable but it becomes nonsensical to say that quality *cannot* be afforded. If we cannot afford quality, we are by definition not meeting customer requirements and we may as well resign ourselves to eventually welcoming the receiver. Either we change our production methods to 'afford' quality or we re-direct the business to another group of customers whose requirements we *can* meet.

While quality must be at the core of a business, it is ultimately only a means to the end of commercial survival (generating sufficient positive cashflow to remain in business) and profit maximisation. Customers' requirements are not met out of altruism but because this is an absolute necessity for commercial success. It is, therefore, implicit that requirements are met at *least cost* (or maximum profit) and the pursuit of quality inevitably involves continual design improvement, production innovation and maximum efficiency. However, the pursuit of least cost does not mean giving the customer less than he expects in the hope that the deficiency will not be noticed. In the long run it will, and the inevitable consequences of failing to meet requirements will have to be faced. Least cost is not skimping on quality; it is delivery of quality in the most efficient manner possible.

A means to minimising costs of production and delivery is *getting it right first time*. Failures and rejects are the (high) costs of not getting it right first and these are just the additional costs arising inside the business. Usually some of the defects go out to customers and the firm incurs the costs of rectification. Even more serious may be the costs entailed in unsatisfied customers and long-term sales decline.

WHY DO WE HAVE TO PURSUE QUALITY?

By now it should be clear that this is an entirely rhetorical question. In any business we have no option other than the pursuit of quality. If we fail to meet their requirements (provide quality), customers will sooner or later switch their business to competitors. Quality is, therefore, a vital *competitive strategy*. Holding our own in a market – just keeping the market share up – requires that we meet customers' requirements at least as well as competitors. Better still, we will aim to meet these requirements better than competitors.

Maximising customer requirements/the pursuit of quality is expressed by some as *delighting* customers. We seek not just broad satisfaction, but meeting requirements in such a manner that they can be said to be delighted. When we achieve this we not only keep customers' business, but they may cease to even consider alternative suppliers.

Going this extra distance to meet customer requirements – delighting them – is in many businesses an attention to the smallest details:

- The equipment control knobs just comfortably fit the hand of the operator.
- The pack can be opened without finding a pair of scissors.
- The consultant's report is titled on the spine (and can, therefore, be found on the client's bookshelf).

Such details are, of course, on top of meeting many other (and generally more major) requirements, but it is such marginal differentiation which gives that edge over competitors.

HOW TO GET (AND KEEP) QUALITY

The traditional approach to quality has focused on the output. This can be described as the 'police' method of quality assurance. Sometimes the policeman is assisted by an ally, the 'fireman'. We will show the limitations of this method and outline the effective alternative of *quality systems*. BS 5750 is a standard for such quality systems.

The Quality Policeman

The quality policeman – quality inspection – is a deeply entrenched part of British management. In principle, the policing works as illustrated in Figure 1.1.

The quality policeman's efforts are entirely focused on the products as they leave the factory (which could equally be a service business office). Product standards (to meet customer requirements) are set and goods tested for conformity. Those meeting the standards go off to the customer and those which do not go for scrap or reworking. What happens inside the black box of the factory is of no real concern to the quality policeman.

There are two fundamental problems inherent in this method of quality assurance: waste is institutionalised and in some businesses the product (or service) cannot be effectively tested for conformity to customer requirements *after* it has been produced.

The problem of institutionalised waste is a necessary feature of quality policing – scrap is the quality department's output and their continued employment depends on a suitable level of waste. If the factory stops sending out faulty products, quality assurance becomes unnecessary. However, this is most unlikely to happen since those who identify the product problems stay outside the production process, and without a feedback system the shop-floor has no opportunity to learn from its mistakes. Of course, in practice the quality policeman does not stay rigidly outside the factory and some attempt is usually made to put things right before faulty products go right through the system.

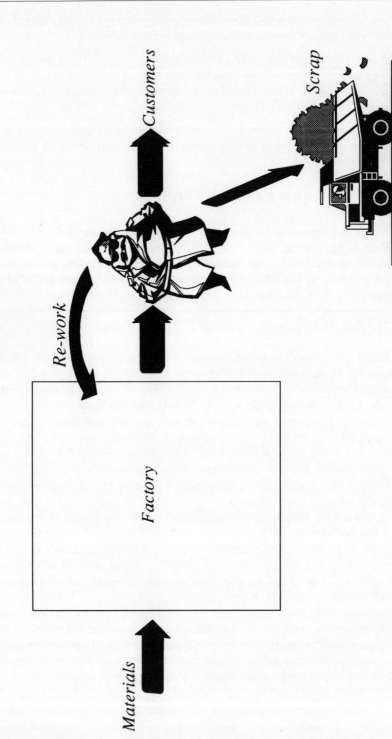

Figure 1.1 The quality policeman

(The later product defects are identified, including after shipping, the higher the costs: the mirror image of added value.) A modified police approach to quality is represented in Figure 1.2. Here the police force has grown and come into the factory, or rather the factory has been split into a number of smaller boxes with quality inspection carried out before the product moves onto the next stage. In principle, however, the problem of institutionalising scrap remains; quality is still outside the production process.

The second problem with a police-based quality system is that product inspection may not be effective. The tests used may not identify non-conformity to requirements. This may be overcome by continuous review of the testing methods and perhaps testing of the testers. However, in many businesses effective quality assurance through post-production testing is just not feasible:

- At a restaurant our requirements are not confined to just receiving food which is edible and tasty. We are also concerned that the waiter deals with us politely. If the waiter mistreats us the damage is done and even if a quality inspector (the head waiter) identifies the 'non-conformance', we are still dissatisfied.
- Satisfaction with a flight will not be improved by the knowledge that incoming planes are checked to see if they have crashed (or even that the causes of a fatal accident are adequately investigated after the event). No, our concern is that something is done to prevent the problem beforehand.
- The value of many professional services depends on opinions being arrived at through professional skills and by adequately trained staff. It may be that the lawyer's advice which costs £500 is no different from a next-door neighbour's, but whose opinion would it be prudent to trust?

These examples have a common requirement for quality assurance; conformity to requirements depends on carrying out work which cannot be adequately or practically tested after the event.

The Fireman

Many a management reputation is built on fire-fighting skills and in their own way firemen are likely to be the hardest working, most resourceful and valuable members of the company's team. Their role in quality assurance is to put right problems as they are identified (by the quality policeman) and it is on the fireman's skill in crisis management that his reputation is built. He is the one who always got the mail through, the product out of the door, come what may, and said that he would manage it somehow, 'even if it kills me'.

Without doubt such heroes are invaluable when things do go wrong, as they always do eventually. However, much of the energy that goes into such fire-fighting would be far better deployed in fire prevention. Moreover, some

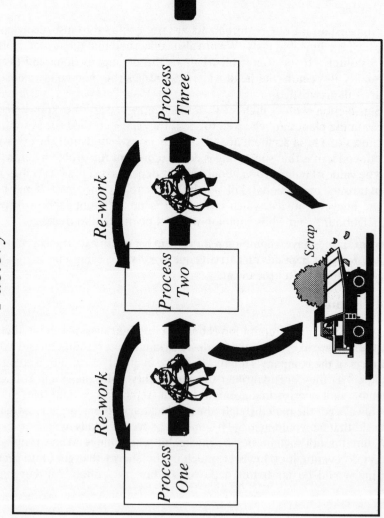

Figure 1.2 The quality policeman and deputies

fire-fighters so love crises that they make no effort to prevent them and may even block others' attempts at improvement.

The £100 Parcel

Scientos made replacement parts for vital medical equipment and had a strong position in this niche market. Although precision manufacture was important, the production skills required were in fact quite low. Scientos's reputation rested wholly on its same-day delivery service.

However, the company was clearly stagnating with few new customers taken on. A new sales director was appointed and his first task was to find out why so few new accounts had been opened in the last year. The answer was easily found: the salesmen spent virtually no time prospecting for new business. They were called in for a severe reprimand.

Naturally the accused had some excuses: 'We have no time. Not only do we have to see our regular customers frequently but we often have to deliver the parts to them as well.' The sales director checked out this story and found it to be substantially true.

The problem went upstairs to board level. The managing director was defensive: 'I hope this isn't a criticism of Bob in despatch. Why, this company's success is very much due to him. He always gets the part to the customer for the time promised.'

'Oh yes, he does', said the sales director. "And how he does it is to wait until there is a panic and then he jumps up and down until one of the sales force gives in and makes the delivery. When that happens, a £10 parcel delivery really costs us £100 in sales time and expenses and it is no wonder we don't have time to chase new business.'

FLYING BY THE BOOK

This has a dull and boring ring to it. But in many situations we take it for granted that things will work because there is a well-established set of rules designed to prevent problems arising in the first place. We expect an oncoming car to stay on the left-hand side of the road and not dodge about as the fancy takes the driver. Flying is an even better example of meticulous procedures designed to ensure that our implicit requirements of safe travel are met. We expect that the crew know what to do if anything does go wrong, that there is an effective emergency procedure and that disaster will not just be averted by the quick thinking of the captain.

The equivalent in business is a *quality system* – an established and proven set of procedures which are revised to take account of a changing environment.

Implementing an effective system increases conformity to customer requirements and, therefore, quality.

QUALITY SYSTEMS AND MEETING REQUIREMENTS

Unlike the police approach to quality assurance, the focus of a quality system is the production process itself and not the output. If we get the recipe right and train the cook, we know the stew will be right; we may still do some tasting before serving-up, but this part of quality assurance is now secondary to good cooking. In time we may stop tasting entirely.

BS 5750 is a standard for such a quality system. Unlike nearly all the other British Standards it is not concerned with a particular product. It is applicable to any situation where a quality system can be applied and, as we will show in later chapters, this means almost any business.

A quality system is put in place after the processes making up a business are analysed and the correct methods are identified – those which ensure the product meets customer requirements. These methods are then systematised and form the quality system. Naturally, the first attempt will not produce a perfect quality system. In fact, perfection will never be achieved, but improvement will be continuous; an essential part of the system will be learning from mistakes.

Tails You Lose And Heads Too

By Friday afternoon we were a bit tired of the consultant leading the quality seminar. I put a real 'stinker' to him:

'Two weeks ago today we had an urgent order to get out to one of our largest customers. At three in the afternoon the Gorman Finisher went out. You know what that meant: we could either get the product off without the final finish and wait for the customer to scream or tell him that we couldn't despatch until Monday midday at best, and we knew that wouldn't do either. So what would you do? What use is the quality system in a real crisis?'

Being the professional he was, the answer came back without hesitation:

'You know your business and your customer. You are the manager, not me. I couldn't possibly advise you on which alternative would leave the customer least dissatisfied. No, what I would do, though, is make sure that we learn from the mistake by investigating why the Gorman went down and what we could have done to lessen that happening. Perhaps you need a back-up finisher or a different maintenance routine? You have to find out. That is the way to use the system to jack up quality in the long term. In other words, have a corrective action procedure in your quality system and use it effectively.'

An effective quality system, therefore, is not just a set of rules for quality production. It is recognised that problems will occur, but the system tries to ensure that they do not keep re-occurring. This is done by procedures for problem identification (eg auditing), investigation (eg corrective action) and long-term rectification (controlled procedure change).

The quality system approach in this book is formal and documented. Anyone involved in a process can refer to a manual and find out what should be done to ensure conformity (although to do it they may need to be qualified or have training – the quality system is not a substitute for skills). In very small businesses high quality is often maintained by an informal quality system kept in the head of key staff; probably the firm's boss who is strongly motivated to give customers whatever they require. However, as the business grows, which it will if it is on a quality track, the informal system breaks down. Several key employees have responsibilities which affect quality and what happens if 'good old Bob' is off on holiday? Moreover, as the staff grows they need to work in the same way, all singing from one sheet.

The Two-Shift Problem

The new plater had been in place at Frith Metal Finishing for six months. It had looked a first-rate piece of kit and the suppliers seemed to have been thorough in the installation. A whole day had been given to operator training with everyone there. All was not well, though, and this was very apparent from the level of customer complaint. The consistency of finish promised was not happening; if anything, the old machine had produced a better finish.

A senior engineer from the equipment supplier was asked to investigate. He arrived at 9 am on Monday and by 10.30 was confident that the problem was easily solved; the machine was just out of setting and by the end of the day shift, testing showed that the finish consistency was now very high.

However, on Tuesday morning the same problems were there again and the engineer recognised that the causes were the same – wrong settings. Again by the end of the shift the output was near perfect. This time the engineer stayed on for the night shift and noticed that as soon as the next foreman arrived he reset the machine, cursing 'those silly b* * * *' as he did so.

'Why have you changed the setting?', asked the engineer. 'To get it right, of course. I remember that when the machine was put in, you people said it had to be set like this for our material.'

The engineer asked to see the page in the procedure manual which set out the settings for the machine.

'And what manual is that? We haven't got one.'

The point of the story is that memory is seldom enough. Important operating procedures need to be documented and available to all who need them. Moreover, when the procedures are changed we have to be sure that all the manuals in use show the revision. Precise documentation and control of that documentation is also, therefore, an essential aspect of a quality system and a requirement of BS 5750.

At any point in time an effective quality system is clear and certain; we know exactly what procedure is to be followed. A business, however, never operates in a static world. Everything changes. As we have already discussed, customers' requirements are fluid. In part, the activities of competitors change expectations. Technological innovation makes it possible to meet requirements in new and more effective ways and all players – customers, competitors and our company – are affected by the macro-economy. Therefore, dynamism must be built into a quality system; otherwise it will become a bureaucratic barrier to adaptation and ultimately prevent the satisfaction of customer requirements. It will become wholly counter-productive.

The pursuit of quality is never-ending and the prime task of any management team is to keep the ball moving up the slope. Figure 1.3 illustrates this concept. The quality system is a chock which prevents backsliding, but it must change as the company moves upwards.

System and commitment

There is undoubtedly a 'gong collection' aspect to BS 5750. Having it has a value independent of what lies behind it. However, to implement a quality system just to get through the BS 5750 assessment is self-defeating. Without the necessary commitment to quality, the business will not prosper in the long run. Having BS 5750 does not increase the value of a bankrupt firm's assets and failure is the eventual cost of a lack of commitment to quality. Moreover, and in the shorter run, a lip-service system may get past the BS 5750 assessors on the first occasion, but what about the surveillance visits? Without real commitment to quality, entropy will ensure the system runs down to a level where accreditation will be lost.

Commitment to quality has to be company-wide and led from the top. If the directors are not convinced that they should be on the quality track, who else can be expected to worry about meeting customer requirements? A quality system is like a new car without petrol: perfect in every respect, but it will not go. The quality fuel is staff attitude and motivation and any business has to address this.

However, this book is about how to put a good car together – a quality system. A reader should look elsewhere to learn about commitment and

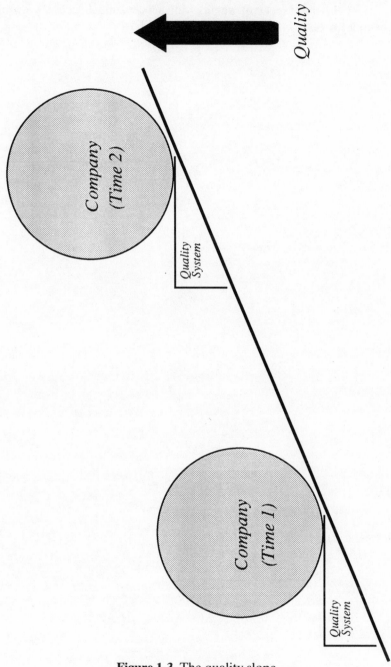

Figure 1.3 The quality slope

motivation. So this aspect of quality will be very much taken for granted throughout the rest of this book. And yet it is vital.

2 BS 5750 – THE STANDARD FOR QUALITY SYSTEMS

Having, in the previous chapter, introduced the concept of quality and quality systems, we can now turn to a standard for quality systems – BS 5750.

In this chapter we describe the scope and the content of BS 5750. The application and relevance of the Standard and the process of certification and registration, ie 'getting' BS 5750, is only mentioned in passing since these topics are covered at some length elsewhere in the book (see Part Two, chapters 5–12).

STANDARDS AND THE BRITISH STANDARDS INSTITUTION

Standards imply a specification against which something can be measured – to establish if it meets the standard – and commonality. A standard is recognised within some community whether that be a single firm, an industry, a country or throughout the world. If something is to a standard of our community, we know that it conforms to whatever specifications are agreed to be appropriate. Standards also imply some recognised method of assessment; in one way or another, we can determine whether or not something meets a standard.

In the UK, standards in a wide range of industrial, business and related activities are *British Standards*, defined by the *British Standards Institution* (BSI). BSI can be traced back to the Engineering Standards Committee set up in 1901. The name was changed in 1918 (to British Engineering Standards Association), received a Royal Charter in 1929 and was renamed British Standards Institution in 1931 to reflect a widening involvement outside engineering.

Today, the BSI is involved in a number of activities. Without doubt, however, its core work remains the creation and revision of standards. This is done through a process of consultation with the great and the good in the field to which the particular standard applies. BS 5750, for example, was prepared by the Quality, Management and Statistics Committee and through the

Technical Committee (QMS/2) upon which some fifty industrial, government and other bodies were represented. No doubt for sound reasons, BSI follows Whitehall methods, and operates through committees with long and precise names, to take account of the many interests affected by introducing or changing a British Standard.

STANDARDS FOR PRODUCTS AND STANDARDS FOR CAPABILITY

All British Standards are defined in published documents. The very large majority of these Standards are *product* Standards – they provide key parameters for a particular product. In a sense, they are recipes; I can use a particular standard to produce a product which matches in the defined parameters someone else's product made to this Standard. Nearly all commercial products have a relevant British Standard, eg:

- BS 1004A: Caterpillar Rollers
- BS 1449: Stainless Steel Tube
- BS 416: Television Sets

Such British Standards have considerable practical value. Not least, buyers and sellers can define a product in a tender, order or contract with reference to the Standard. As a buyer, I am assured that a product meeting this Standard will be to a specification which I have decided meets my technical requirements – the product meets my technical *quality* needs. Equally, as a supplier, I know the key technical parameters which I need to meet in the product in order to satisfy my customer. So, a BS saves both buyer and seller considerable work in defining the product and gives both a basis for quality assurance.

The buyer and seller may of course choose, and often do, to set additional specifications over and above that covered in the BS, but even so the BS provides a framework within which refinements can be added. To increase confidence that the product fully meets the BS, the buyer may seek (or the seller may offer) the assurance of certification through a Kitemark (from BSI) or a similar scheme offered by other bodies. The concept of such independent assessment of conformity to a BS will be discussed shortly.

In principle, a product can be verified against the particular British Standard; the Standard will provide sufficient technical details to provide a basis for tests to establish whether or not the defined characteristics are present. As such, however, this type of BS has nothing to say about how the product should be made to arrive at the specification. Testing for conformity to a BS is, therefore, a suitable role for the quality 'policeman' introduced in the previous chapter. The manufacture of a product conforming to a BS may involve a high or low level of efficiency with consequently high or low scrap levels, and may not necessarily meet the customer's requirements (who may need a product differing in some way from the BS). To meet a different type of requirement, therefore, BSI also have Standards relating to *capabilities* as well as products.

Product and capability standards are complementary rather than alternatives. Consider road safety: the design and condition of cars on the road affects safety standards. The manufacturer of new cars ensures in a myriad of ways that vehicles meet acceptable safety levels – the brakes are capable of stopping, the steering is precise, seat belts effective etc. Periodic testing (the MOT) also addresses vehicle standards to ensure that in key areas the car's safety features have not deteriorated below an acceptable level. However, although vital, such product standards cannot alone make the streets safe. Cars do not yet drive themselves and we insist on setting capability standards for drivers and an appropriate testing system – the driving test.

BS 5750 is such a capability standard. It is the standard for Quality Systems and addresses how the product or service is produced rather than *what* is produced. Two companies can both make a similar product to a common *product* BS, but under widely different production methods. Another two companies may make completely different things – one could produce a service with no physical content – but use a comparable system to maximise the quality of their output. BS 5750 provides a recognised standard for a quality system and both these firms could successfully meet it despite the very wide differences in their activities.

STANDARDS AND ASSESSMENT

As we have already stated, any type of standard implies assessment; the process of establishing conformity to the standard. A standard which cannot be assessed is in practice of no use; if we have no way of knowing whether or not we have met a standard, why have it in the first place?

There are three types of assessment – first, second and third (or independent) party. In the case of a product, the supplier can simply assert that what is offered conforms to a published standard. Obviously, there are limitations to the value of such assessment. In a less than perfect world, the buyer may well feel that such assessment lacks objectivity, because it is not in the supplier's interest to admit it, if, in some way or other, the product does not meet the Standard. However, this is not to say that such assessment is always worthless. In fact, it is part of trading in good faith; we often, and rightly, count on suppliers' honesty. As a last resort, claims may be legally enforceable through the purchase contract.

Second party assessment involves the customer establishing, through appropriate means, that what is offered by the supplier meets the standards that he, the customer, requires. The customer, therefore, carries out tests on the products supplied or, in the case of a capability standard, vets the procedures used within the supplier's organisation. Such assessment is effective since the two parties to the transaction which matter most (buyer and seller) are involved and satisfied. Second party assessment can, however, be costly and inconvenient.

If a factory supplies a number of customers with the same product and they all wish to be assured that the standard claimed is being met, the same tests will be duplicated with the costs multiplied by the number of customers concerned. If a capability standard is involved, the process of vetting the factory will be duplicated. One or other group of suppliers' assessors may never be off the premises and the costs of production will increase through disruption or employing staff to deal with less than welcome visitors.

Third party or independent assessment is carried out by a body which customers are likely to recognise as authoritative – because a product has been assessed by BSI or similar bodies, its adherence to the relevant standards will accepted. Furthermore, if a company has undergone third party assessment, it is quite likely that new customers will consider it as a supplier. Third party assessment is, therefore, commercially valuable to a company.

All British Standards can be assessed by a third party and this includes BS 5750. An organisation 'gets' BS 5750 by being assessed by a recognised assessor and agreeing to regular inspection/surveillance by this same body. If successful in this, it is then qualified for inclusion on the *Register of Quality Assessed United Kingdom Companies* (published by a Government Department, the DTI). In the UK, the National Accreditation Council for Certification Bodies in turn assesses and accredits assessor/certification bodies.

It is worth emphasising that assessment for BS 5750 does not necessarily involve the BSI. As mentioned earlier, BSI has a number of roles and this includes, through its inspectorate, assessment of firms. The Institution, however, does not have a monopoly in this work. A company seeking to have its quality system assessed to BS 5750 may choose to use BSI as assessors, but there are other competing and accredited (by NACCB) assessors such as Lloyd's, Yarsley, Bureau Veritas, to name but a few. There are also some non-accredited assessors offering their services and these too can be considered. (The subject is discussed in some detail in chapter 11.)

BS 5750 – THE STANDARD

The Standard for quality systems, BS 5750, has it origins in military supply. Because of the critical nature of these products and the practical problems of investigating faulty products used in action, emphasis was placed on how the products were made and the quality systems of the suppliers concerned. Standards for appropriate quality systems were set, including at international level (NATO) and with corresponding national standards for co-operating and allied governments. In the UK there is a range of Defence Standards, eg 05-21.

As such standards became established and known throughout industry, demand grew for something comparable outside the defence field. Eventually, in 1979, this led to BS 5750. The revised 1987 version of BS 5750 was more comprehensive in scope and remains today the recognised and accepted Standard for quality systems.

Not only was BS 5750 drafted to cover activities outside military supply, it was also intended to be universally applicable. BS 5750 can be applied, therefore, to the quality systems of all commercial organisations (and some non-commercial ones as well). This means that it is not just relevant to manufacturers; it is equally relevant to suppliers of services. However, a service provider is unlikely to be encouraged by a reading of the BS 5750 Standard. The language, terminology and apparent assumptions are clearly more friendly to the manufacturer than service provider. Even manufacturers outside the engineering field may feel that the Standard is not written with their businesses in mind. Despite this, BS 5750 is intended to have universal application and in practice the 'manufacturing' elements of the Standard can in all cases be adapted to meet the situation of even the most service-based business.

So far we have referred to BS 5750 as one Standard. It is in fact a series, published in separate documents, Part 0 to Part 13 (but with gaps, eg Parts 5 and 6 are no longer current). These are listed in Table 2.1 along with 'ISO 9000 Series' references; the latter is an equivalent international Standard and will be discussed shortly.

The Parts of the Standard fall into two groups. Firstly there are the quality system requirements themselves – Parts 1, 2, 3 and the Stockist Schemes. A company seeking registration under the Standard opts to be assessed under only one of these Parts (although it is possible for different sites, branches or activities of one company to seek registration under different Parts) and when an assessment is carried out, it is against one of these Parts. Success or failure depends on demonstrating that the quality requirements set out in Parts 1, 2 or 3 have been met.

Table 2.1 *BS 5750 and ISO 9000 Series*

	BS 5750	ISO 9000 Series
Guide to selection and use of appropriate part of the Standard	Part 0/0.1	9000
Guide to overall quality management and system elements	Part 0/0.2	9004

Quality specifications for:

Design/development production installation and servicing	Part 1	9001
Producing to a customer's specification (or published specification)	Part 2	9002
Final inspection and testing	Part 3	9003
Scheme for stockists (equivalent to Part 2)	Registered stockists scheme – Levels A & B	–
Guide to use of Parts 1, 2 & 3	Part 4	–
Guide to quality management and quality elements for services	Part 8	9004 – 2
Guide to the application of BS 5750 Part 1 to the development, supply and maintenance of software	Part 13 (TickIT Initiative)	–

Note: Further guideline Parts to the Standard are planned: Parts 7, 9, 10, 11 and 12.

The second group of Parts to BS 5750 – Parts 0 (01/02), 4, 8 and 13 – have a different status. They are notes providing guidance and advice and whatever is contained in these Parts are not in themselves requirements that have to be met.

> This Part of BS 5750 does not add any requirements to those in BS 5750 Parts 1, 2 and 3. Care should be taken that the guidance given, which may suggest various methods of providing assurance, is not used in place of, or as additional requirements to, those given in Parts 1, 2 and 3.
>
> *(Foreword to BS 5750 Part 4)*

In other words, the guidance of Part 4 (as well as Parts 0 and 8) does not have to be followed, although the fact that it is offered by the body responsible for the Parts which contain the requirements should not be ignored.

As a minimum, a reader deciding to seek assessment and registration for BS 5750 must obtain a copy (around ten pages only in length) of whichever of Parts 1, 2 or 3 (or the Stockist Scheme) is relevant to his or her own business; *which* part is relevant will be discussed shortly. Companies involved in software must also take account of Part 13, 'TickIT'. Sight of other Parts is arguably not vital, although at least a readthrough will do no harm.

The ISO 9000 Series is the equivalent international standard for quality systems and, like BS 5750, is available as a series of documents. Give or take some differences in how it is expressed, the contents of the ISO 9000 Series are the same as BS 5750 with the key Parts having an ISO 9000 Series equivalent. (See Table 2.1 and, for example, BS 5750 Part 1/ISO 9001.) This equivalence is not a coincidence. The ISO 9000 Series was modelled on BS 5750 which, internationally, was the pioneering standard for quality systems. So now for some really good news. A company meeting the requirements of BS 5750 (whichever part is appropriate) also meets the requirements of the equivalent of the ISO 9000 Series and if assessment and registration is obtained for eg BS 5750 Part 1, this is accepted as a satisfactory assessment for eg ISO 9001. Two for the price of one.

The practical value of the equivalence of BS 5750 and ISO 9000 lies in exporting or carrying out business throughout the single market of the EC. In all industrialised countries there is a national standard for quality systems compatible with ISO 9000 and therefore assessment and registration for BS 5750 has worldwide recognition and commercial value. See Table 2.2 for corresponding national quality system standards.

So far we have not considered the differences between the Parts of BS 5750 which define the requirements for a quality system – Parts 1, 2, 3 and the Stockist scheme. In essence the differences are very simply stated: Parts 2, 3 and the Stockists scheme are as Part 1, but with some requirements of Part 1 omitted. In particular, Part 2 omits the requirements for *design* and a linked element, *servicing*; Part 3 also omits several other elements found in Part 2 (the specifics are shown in Table 2.1 on page 31). The Stockist scheme is very similar in scope to Part 2 but, as its name suggests, is geared to the needs of businesses who stock (factor) rather than make.

Which Part of BS 5750 is applicable to a particular business depends on the commercial activities undertaken. Part 1 is clearly for businesses engaged in design as part of their production process; it is the contents and requirements of this Part which will be discussed in some detail next.

BS 5750 PART 1

BS 5750 Part 1 defines the standard for and requirements of a quality system under twenty main headings of its Section 4, numbered 4.1 to 4.20 (Sections 0–3 are essentially introductory in coverage). The two requirements of Part 1 which distinguish it from other Parts are *Design Control – 4.4* and *Servicing – 4.19*. Arguably, of these, Design Control is the more important, if only because it appears that servicing is regarded as necessarily bound up with design. Servicing may be needed because a design activity is carried on and not vice versa.

Table 2.2 International quality system standards

Country	Specification For Design/Development, Production, Installation And Servicing	Specification For Production And Installation	Specification For Final Inspection And Test
International	**ISO 9001: 1987**	**ISO 9002: 1987**	**ISO 9003: 1987**
Australia	AS 3901	AS 3902	AS 3903
Austria	OE NORM-PREN 29001	OE NORM-PREN 29002	OE NORM-PREN 29003
Belgium	NBN X 50-003	NBN X 50-004	NBN X 50-005
China	GB/T 10300.2-88	GB/T 10300.3-88	GB/T 10300.4-88
Denmark	DS/EN 29001	DS/EN 29002	DS/EN 29003
Finland	SFS-ISO 9001	SFS-ISO 9002	SFS-ISO 9003
France	NF X 50-131	NF X 50-132	NF X 50-133
Germany	DIN ISO 9001	DIN ISO 9002	DIN ISO 9003
Holland	NEN-ISO 9001	NEN-ISO 9002	NEN-ISO 9003
Hungary	MI 18991 - 1988	NI 18992 - 1988	NI 18993 - 1988
India	IS: 10201 Part 4	IS: 10201 Part 5	IS: 10201 Part 6
Ireland	IS 300 Part 1/ISO 9001	IS 300 Part 2/ISO 9002	IS 300 Part 3/ISO 9003
Italy	UNI/EW 29001 - 1987	UNI/EN 29002 - 1987	UNI/EN 29003 - 1987
Malaysia	MS 985/ISO 9001 - 1987	MS 985/ISO 9002 - 1987	MS 985/ISO 9003 - 1987
New Zealand	NZS 5601 - 1987	NZS 5602 - 1987	NZS 5603 - 1987
Norway	NS-EN 29001: 1988	NS-ISO 9002	NS-ISO 9003
South Africa	SABS 0157: Part 1	SABS 0157: Part II	SABS 0157: Part III
Spain	UNE 66 901	UNE 66 902	UNE 66 903
Sweden	SS-ISO 9001: 1988	SS-ISO 9002: 1988	SS-ISO 9003: 1988
Switzerland	SN-ISO 9001	SN-ISO 9002	SN-ISO 9003
Tunisia	NT 100.19 - 1987	NT 110.20 - 1987	NT 110.21 - 1987
United Kingdom	**BS5750: Part 1:**	**BS5750: 1987: Part 2:**	**BS5750: 1987: Part 3:**
USA	ANSI/ASQC 091	ANSI/ASQC 092	ANSI/ASQC 093
USSR	40.9001 - 88	40.9002 - 88	-
Yugoslavia	JUS A.K. 1.012	JUS A.K. 1.013	JUS A.K. 1.014
European Comunity (CEN)	EN 29001	EN 29002	EN 29003

In BS 5750 Part 1 the meaning of *design* is much the same as in normal language. A firm carrying out design takes the responsibility for arriving at a product, meeting a defined customer requirement:

- An architect designs a building to meet the space requirements of his clients.
- A software house writes a system to provide a specific information requirement.
- A crane maker designs an overhead crane for a particular factory.
- A management consultant designs a programme of consultancy to solve defined problems of a client company.

In these examples a *particular* customer's requirements are defined and then a product or service is designed to match. Equally, however, products or services are designed for customers who are unknown until a sale is made from stock. Volvo did not design the 850 range specifically to meet a particular individual's personal requirements – it just so happens that he falls within the segment of the car-buying population whose requirements such a car meets. Design of this type is obviously very common throughout manufacturing industry. However, in such cases the design process itself is not part of the contract with the customer – he only agrees to buy because the off-the-shelf product meets his needs. For this reason companies involved in supply from stock will normally seek BS 5750 Part 2 rather than Part 1. Similarly, Part 2 is appropriate where there is no design activity at all and instead the customer provides a precise product or service specification. A jobbing engineering shop is, for example, given detailed drawings of the component to be produced, together with a material and manufacturing specification. The customer expects the product to be the same as might be made in-house or by an alternative supplier. In this case BS 5750 Part 2 rather than Part 1 is appropriate.

In the opinion of the authors, the arrangement of the twenty sub-clauses of Section 4 of Part 1 is not reader-friendly. In Figure 2.1, therefore, we have re-arranged the twenty sub-clauses into an order which we believe is more analytically useful. However, the reader must be aware that this re-arrangement is ours and not BSI's, and if this leads to any unintended misinterpretation we apologise in advance (we hope and believe it does not).

In Figure 2.1, the twenty sub-clauses of the quality requirements for BS 5750 Part 1 are shown in italics and arranged in three major blocks labelled in non-BSI terms. The central block of nine clauses is, in our opinion, the core of the requirements, since these concern what happens in the 'operating process' itself. Very broadly, this term covers inputs, what is done with these inputs, ie the process, and the outputs, ie what goes out to customers. The clauses in the left and right blocks have a supporting rather than core role but *are every bit as essential as those in the central 'Operating Process' block.* To meet the Standard a quality system must be shown to meet the requirements of 'Quality System

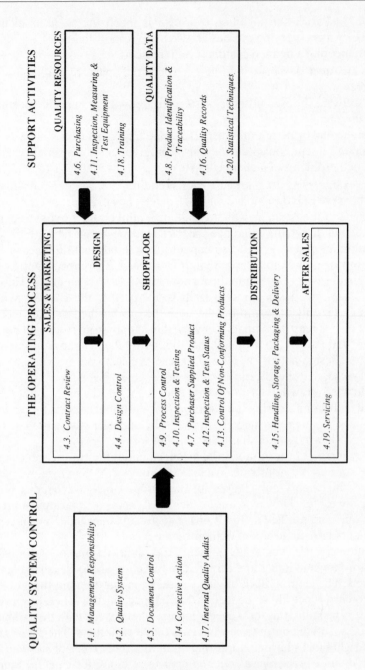

Figure 2.1 BS 5750 Part 1 (ISO 9001)

Control' and 'Support Activities' as fully as those included in 'Operating Process'.

We shall now discuss the contents of all the requirements starting with those we have included within 'The Operating Process'. As we have already mentioned, a reader intending to be personally involved in designing a quality system to meet BS 5750 should, in due course, obtain and read the Standard itself.

4.3 Contract Review

We argued in chapter 1 that quality is meeting the customer's requirements. Clearly, to meet requirements we must know them. Contract review is concerned, therefore, with adequately defining and documenting these requirements (including variations from any set out in a tender, or which arise during the contract period), and establishing that the resources needed to meet them are available. What should be covered in such a record of requirements and how it should be documented will vary from business to business.

In a bespoke or jobbing type of business (eg printing, construction, many services) the contract review appropriately precedes any design or production activities and, therefore, fits logically as shown in Table 2.2. However, in businesses supplying from stock, contract review would follow production of the product or service and would determine whether the available, ex-stock products met requirements. In Figure 2.1 the Contract Review inner box would be shown between *4.15* 'Handling etc' and *4.19* 'Servicing'.

A final point is that Contract Review follows drawing up the contract or tendering and is in effect, therefore, after the marketing process: activities which are not explicitly covered in BS 5750. Similarly, other activities vital to the survival of any business are also not covered. The most obvious omission is the accounting function. This does not mean that functions such as marketing and accounting have no quality dimension – clearly they have – but they are not formally addressed by the Standard and in the assessment process for BS 5750 a company is not evaluated in these areas.

4.4 Design Control

Design Control is a particularly vital requirement of BS 5750 Part 1 because, along with Servicing, its inclusion distinguishes the Standard from Part 2. Starting from an adequate definition of the requirements of the customer (in a bespoke business this will be defined in the Contract Review or follow soon after), design work must be carried out by qualified staff, equipped with appropriate resources to produce a design matching the requirements. The specific activities involved here will, as with all requirements of the Standard, vary widely according to the type of business. The qualifications required to carry out design work on a nuclear reactor are obviously very different from the skills required to prepare a questionnaire in a market research company.

Design Control requirements also cover the need to verify designs (and establish criteria for verification) and control the output documents. Once a design is established, it is essential that it is that specific design which is used and not an earlier and superseded draft. This will involve some sort of document control and identification procedure.

The next four BS 5750 Part 1 requirements can be thought of as happening on the 'shop floor': what is actually done while making the product or providing the service to ensure that it meets requirements.

4.9 Process Control

The requirement of this heading is that the work process itself shall be carried out in a controlled way. This includes documenting how the process is to be carried out, providing suitable written instructions for those involved and monitoring what happens during the process. For example, is the operating temperature of the furnace within the correct limits? Have the fire sensors been installed in the positions specified in the drawings? Also by what criteria is the output acceptable?

Special mention is made of the requirements of 'special' processes, by which is meant those whose output cannot be adequately tested after manufacture and prior to customer delivery. Many service activities are in this category.

4.10 Inspection And Testing

Inspection and testing is concerned with establishing whether the inputs into the work process, the outputs and work at various stages in between, meet defined requirements. The inputs may be bought-in materials.

A special type of input is customer-supplied product, eg a component which we are going to finish in some way in our factory. This is covered in a separate heading of the Standard – *4.7 Purchaser Supplied Product*. In this case the requirement includes appropriate inspection, but also addresses the need to look after our customer's product, to make sure it is his which is processed and that its condition does not deteriorate while in our charge. In the wording of the Standard, a *supplier* is the company registered for BS 5750 – 'us' – while the *purchaser* is our customer.

It is worth noting that inspection and testing of output is an explicit requirement of the Standard, even though an effective system should not depend only on inspection and testing. Arguably, the better the system the less the need for after-the-event inspection. The quality 'policeman' should have a reducing role and in an ideal world be redundant entirely.

4.12 Inspection And Test Status / 4.13 Control Of Non-Conforming Products

If we are carrying out testing to verify quality, it is essential that we know which inputs, outputs and in-process products have been tested; also, which tests and inspections have been applied. In the case of the final product, we must establish that it is up to standard prior to despatch to the customer; that the appropriate tests have been carried out. Stamps, labelling, location in the process area, together with various records, may all be used as suitable methods of meeting this requirement.

If, when testing products, we identify some which do not meet requirements, these must be controlled so that they are not mixed with satisfactory products. Marking and location in a special area prior to reworking or scrapping, may be appropriate methods of meeting this requirement for the control of such non-conforming products (*4.13*).

The final two requirements which we have included in our production process grouping concern looking after our quality product after it has been made.

4.15 Handling, Storage, Packaging And Delivery

Very simply, this requirement addresses the need to keep the product in the required condition after it leaves the 'shop floor' and before it reaches the customer. It must be handled (moved within our premises), stored prior to despatch, packed for delivery and delivered in a way that neither damages it nor allows it to deteriorate. The latter may limit the shelf life of the product.

Appropriate methods to meet this requirement obviously depend on the product involved; lifting builders' sand in a mechanical shovel is appropriate for that product, but not for a mainframe computer. In the case of some services, addressing some of these requirements may just not be realistic, eg how should we handle a consultant's report (with scepticism?) It is, therefore, an important point that while *all* the requirements of the Standard have to be carefully considered in the context of a particular business, a few may not be practically applicable.

4.19 Servicing

This is explicitly applicable in only some situations, despite the fact that this is a clause distinguishing Part 1 from Part 2 of the Standard: *Where servicing is specified in the contract* . . . If such servicing is specified, procedures are required to make sure that servicing work is carried out as required. If the contract with the customer does not specify servicing, then there is no requirement to meet. It is worth mentioning, however, that some businesses may choose to include in their quality system something approaching servicing, even where it is not a contractual requirement. This may include various forms of customer follow-up. Over and above the formal requirements of BS 5750, a company seeking registration for the Standard should consider including in its quality system critical elements affecting long-term customer satisfaction; in this way gaining BS 5750 will be more than simply 'gong collection'.

The various requirements of the Standard grouped as 'Support Activities' are not integral to the production process, but are needed if the quality system is to be successfully implemented. They fall into two sub-groups: Quality Resources and Quality Data.

Three requirements – clauses *4.6, 4.11* and *4.18* – ensure that the resources applied within production are appropriate to quality needs. *Purchasing (4.6)* covers setting up procedures to ensure that supplies bought into the production process meet requirements. Specifics mentioned in this clause concern the selection and assessment of suppliers (the term 'sub-contractor' is used), documenting the supply process so that suppliers know precisely what we need to meet our requirements and verifying that what is supplied is what is required.

The requirements of 'purchasing' do not, it is worth noting, require that on implementing a system we start from scratch and minutely scrutinise suppliers we have dealt with perfectly happily for years. That we have dealt with them to our satisfaction should more than qualify their inclusion in an approved supplier list (which is commonly one element of an appropriate purchasing procedure). Neither do our suppliers have to be BS 5750 registered themselves. However, to satisfy ourselves that their supplies are to our requirements, we may decide that we need assurance of *their* quality system and BS 5750 may be the most practical means for them to give such assurance.

If we are carrying out inspection and testing within the production process, we must ensure that any instruments or equipment we use in this activity are capable of providing appropriate results, eg the micrometer is accurate enough to measure whether our component is within the required range of tolerance. *Inspection, measuring and test equipment (4.11)* is the requirement of the Standard to meet this need. It covers procedures for selecting appropriate equipment for the test, calibrating and checking its accuracy and ensuring that it is kept up to an appropriate standard. The application of this requirement in some service businesses may present problems.

The third class of quality resource included is people – *Training (4.18)*. Even the most automated of plant is dependent on staff being trained to meet the needs of the job while in some businesses quality output is almost wholly dependent on the skills of those involved. Any business committed to quality must address and plan training needs.

BS 5750 requires records to demonstrate that the quality activities are carried out. Throughout the clauses of the Standard discussed above, the need for records is specifically mentioned. There are also requirements for quality data – means of identifying products and therefore tracing them through the production process, keeping records and the use of statistical techniques in evaluating quality data.

We can only have quality records on a specific product (or product batch or, in the case of some services, a project) if we can identify it. The requirements of *Product Identification And Traceability (4.8)* can certainly be met by physically labelling products, eg stamping the machine with a unique number. We can then examine the quality records relating to this specific product. Other products cannot be labelled in this way, eg bulk deliveries of flour, but we can nevertheless relate a batch of the product, through records, to the specific processes carried out. For example, we know that the flour delivered on 1 March to the bakery was part a batch from a particular silo and that this was milled on 12 February during the third shift.

To be of use, quality records must be filed systematically, retained for an appropriate time – product life may be the criteria here – kept up to date and be in a usable form. They do not have to be in paper form; electronic data is an alternative. These requirements are specified in *Quality Records (4.16)*.

In reading BS 5750 Part 1, the requirement very briefly specified in *Statistical Techniques (4.20)* seems both odd and out of place. It only becomes sensible once it is understood that the application of statistical techniques is either important (as per Philip Crosby) or the kernel (as per Edward Deming*) of quality 'schools'. The concept can also be traced to the philosophical position that we can only know what we can measure.

The cynical might consider that this apparently gratuitous inclusion of statistical techniques in the Standard was a sop to some of the great and the good involved in drawing it up. However, this would be a shame, because even simple statistics can be a very effective tool in quality control and it does not require more than the most rudimentary numerical skills to apply many statistical tools. An example is keeping a record by time of the number of jams in the machine, graphing these and recording on the same sheet the types of material going through. We may be able to show that only a few materials have more than a certain level of jams per hour. We might then trace the problem to one supplier and consider how a quality defect might be resolved at the purchasing stage.

A quality system includes the procedures carried out within and in support of the production processes. From another perspective, however, a quality system must be documented, reviewed and updated in line with changes in the environment. Mechanisms are also needed to identify deficiencies in either the operation or the content of the system. This aspect of a quality system is covered in BS 5750 Part 1 through five clauses which we have grouped together under 'Quality System Control'.

---

*Deming and Crosby are among the best known 'quality gurus'. Each has his own philosophy and methodology but the result of their work (and the work of others such as Juran and Feigenbaum) has been to make quality a key issue. Ironically, although American, Deming's greatest influence has been in Japan where he enjoys the status of a national hero. Crosby's fame is based on books including *Quality is Free* and *Quality Without Tears*.

A quality system does not just happen. It is a major management task to both introduce an effective system and maintain it. At the top of the company a policy decision has to be made in relation to quality, a *quality policy*. Typically, this is a one-page statement from which the system follows. The responsibilities for implementing each part of the quality system also have to be defined and with usually one person co-ordinating (the *Management Representative*). Special attention must also be given for responsibility for inspection and testing. Finally, the working of a quality system must be periodically considered and decisions made about necessary changes. All these requirements are covered in BS 5750 Part 1 in *Management Responsibility (4.1)*.

The clause of the Standard *Quality System (4.2)* (strangely worded, since the whole is a standard for quality systems) might be better titled if it included 'documented'. The requirement in this respect is two-fold; the system must be documented and this shall describe how the system is to be implemented. Typically 'how' is covered by a procedure manual.

The document containing the quality system is also required to be controlled – *Document Control (4.5)*. This includes an approval process for the contents, the availability to all concerned of *up-to-date* copies and procedures for changing/updating the documents or parts of it as changes in the system are agreed (again by some controlled method).

Everywhere things go wrong. No matter how rigorous the quality system, the standard of the plant and the training and motivation of the workforce, problems will occur. Such problems are reflected in the output: products are 'non-conforming' to quality requirements. The Standard's requirements for *Corrective Action (4.14)* cover procedures for the identification of such deficiencies, actions taken to investigate their cause and to prevent recurrence. The latter may lead to a need for a change in the quality system which might have to be considered by a management review *(4.1)* and brought about through the provisions for document control *(4.5)*.

Lastly, it is a requirement that deficiencies identified are not only dealt with but are also actively sought out through *Internal Quality Audits (4.17)*. Such audits must be carried out systematically (to a schedule and method) and may lead to *Corrective Actions* and again to review and change. Internal audits mirror the work carried out by external assessors (the bodies whose report leads to BS 5750 registration) and are therefore essential as part of the process of approval. However, and more important, they can be a vital tool in quality enhancement and consequently commercial success.

Standards such as BS 5750 have been criticised for being static. It is said that they ensure adherence to a given standard of quality and in effect inhibit the dynamic process of quality enhancement. In our view, such a problem only arises through poor implementation of a quality system – perhaps where BS 5750 is sought purely as a 'gong collection' exercise. An effective quality system builds in dynamic quality improvement. The triad shown in Figure 2.2 provides

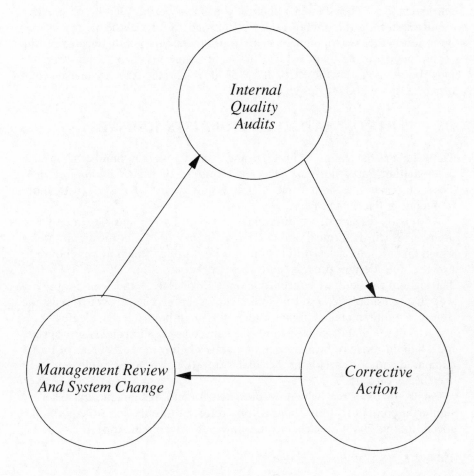

Figure 2.2 The quality triad

an effective quality improvement motor. Internal Quality Audits identify deficiencies which are investigated through Corrective Action with recommendations made for change. These are considered at a Management Review and change in the Quality System is agreed and implemented. In turn, the revised procedures are audited and if deficiencies are still found the process is repeated.

We have now covered all the requirements of BS 5750 Part 1. It should be clear that the Standard itself is general, can be applied to all businesses with a design element (we will eleborate this point elsewhere), but has to be interpreted and implemented to meet the needs and circumstances of a particular firm. The Standard defines what must be included in an effective quality system, but it cannot *itself* be followed. Nearly all of the rest of this book covers the development of an appropriate quality system: one to meet the requirements of the Standard. Before completing this chapter, however, we must briefly consider the Parts of BS 5750 which meet the circumstances of organisations without a design element.

BS 5750 PARTS 2 AND 3 AND STOCKISTS SCHEMES

Table 2.3 lists the clauses of Part 1, 2 and 3 and shows their numbering in each case. Neither Part 2 nor Part 3 has any requirements which are *not* in Part 1. They do, however, omit some of the requirements of Part 1 (with more omissions in Part 3 than Part 2).

As already discussed, the differences between Parts 1 and 2 lie in only two areas of which the critical one is *Design Control*. Part 2 is for organisations which are without a design function or with a design function but choose to exclude the design process and seek registration for BS 5750 Part 2. Throughout the book we concentrate on BS 5750 Parts 1 and 2 and for brevity we will often simply refer to BS 5750, except where it is necessary to discuss the different requirements of organisations with or without a design element.

Part 3 of the Standard has a fairly specialised application and is appropriate for a limited range of businesses (comparatively few are registered for Part 3 compared with for Parts 1 and 2). Therefore, we have chosen not to comment specifically on Part 3.

Finally the Stockist Scheme – designed for non-manufacturers – is very similar in content to Part 2 and will be referred to only occasionally. Some specific points about the Scheme are, however, covered in Appendix 1.

Table 2.3 *BS 5750 Parts 1, 2 and 3*

Requirement	BS 5750 Clause Nomenclature		
	Part 1	Part 2	Part 3
Management responsibility	4.1	4.1	4.1
Quality system	4.2	4.2	4.2
Contract review	4.3	4.3	
Design control	4.4		
Document control	4.5	4.4	4.3
Purchasing	4.6	4.5	

Purchaser supplied products	4.7	4.6	
Product identification and traceability	4.8	4.7	4.4
Process control	4.9	4.8	
Inspection and testing	4.10	4.9	4.5
Inspection measuring and test equipment	4.11	4.10	4.6
Inspection and test status	4.12	4.11	4.7
Control of non-conforming products	4.13	4.12	4.8
Corrective action	4.14	4.13	
Handling, storage, packaging and delivery	4.15	4.14	4.9
Quality records	4.16	4.15	4.10
Internal quality audits	4.17	4.16	
Training	4.18	4.17	4.11
Servicing	4.19		
Statistical techniques	4.20	4.18	4.12

3 DO YOU WANT BS 5750?

This chapter will help the reader decide whether BS 5750 is worthwhile for his own organisation. We describe the major benefits and also consider the drawbacks. We then discuss the relevance of BS 5750: what type of company and organisation can sensibly consider an application?

THE BENEFITS

Chapter 1 covered the general benefits of quality and quality systems. BS 5750 is not synonymous with quality systems. A company can gain the general benefits of a quality system without BS 5750 registration. Many do so. We believe, however, that BS 5750 offers gains over and above such general advantages of a quality system, as well as improving the effectiveness of the system. It is these specific benefits of BS 5750 on which we shall concentrate.

The benefits are both external and internal. First the external ones. The strongest argument for a company going for BS 5750 is that this may become necessary to keep major business (as is illustrated in the case opposite).

The largest organisations (and in all markets these are the largest customers) almost always have formalised quality systems and are often themselves BS 5750 registered. Control of supplies is a vital element in any quality system and there is increasingly a tendency to limit dealings to suppliers who can demonstrate that, in turn, they have an effective quality system in place. Often this simply translates into a requirement that suppliers have BS 5750. Those who are not registered to the Standard are not believed to take quality seriously. The Government, the largest customer in the country, is one of the organisations taking this line. At a recent meeting organised by the DTI for management consultants a spokesman said: 'If you are not approved to BS 5750 in two years' time we will assume that you plan to retire from the business.' The requirement for supplier registration for BS 5750 is not, therefore, confined to suppliers of physical products.

We can't deal with you any more, Joe

Joe Burns had always been committed to quality and over the years this had paid off well. Burns Technics produced highly specialised components and the investment he put into both equipment and people made Burns the leader in a niche market. The largest customer by far was a recently privatised utility with whom Burns had sole supplier status.

Joe had been asked to visit Tom Howell, the engineering buyer of the utility. As far as he knew, there was no problem with the products or the delivery. In fact, only last month a technical manager had gone out of his way to commend Burns to his opposite number in another major utility. Still Joe was uneasy. Tom had not seemed his normal, affable self and there had been those letters asking for details of Burns' quality systems. If he had a failing, Joe knew that it was his paperwork. Anyway, why ask about the quality system when the excellent quality of Burns was a byword in the industry? Perhaps the letters were just a hangover from the bad old bureaucratic days before privatisation.

The meeting with Tom started off well; the usual pleasantries about wives, children, dogs and golf and enquiries about the latest delivery from Burns suggested there was no problem in this area. But then Tom got to the point of the meeting.

'I will be blunt, Joe. As things stand, I won't be able to put any more orders with you after July.'

'But I have had no complaints from you about the products and I am sure we can discuss the money side of things if you have had other quotes.'

'Well, Queros are very keen to do business and can supply all our requirements, but I have doubts about them. However, I will have no choice. Look at this from the top.'

Tom passed across a memo headed 'Technical Suppliers and BS 5750'.

'In six months time I can only buy from suppliers who are registered for BS 5750. The only exception is if no available source has BS 5750. Queros have. I understand from our quality department that you have not replied at all to their enquiries.'

The strongest case for seeking BS 5750, therefore, is that without it a company will no longer be able to supply some of its major customers. BS 5750 may be the price that has to be paid to keep a substantial slice of business. It may be a condition of survival. Even in our story of Joe Burns, a supplier has fair warning of what is coming. However, it generally takes about a year from scratch for a company to obtain BS 5750 and that is assuming everything goes well. The timetable imposed by a major customer may not be long enough.

Moreover, it is better to work to your own timetable than someone else's. Also there are definite marketing benefits of taking the initiative.

Clearly, the reader must consider what is happening in his or her own industry when weighing the likelihood that BS 5750 will be a formal requirement even to quote for business. In the authors' view there are few industries untouched by BS 5750. A limitation on even the largest customers, however, is that they cannot require BS 5750 approval of their suppliers if none of them have it. If no management consultancy has sought BS 5750, the DTI will be hard put to buy only from those who are registered. An assessment of the potential requirement for BS 5750, therefore, should consider both customers' indications and whether or not competitors are going down this road. Once started, however, the momentum can rapidly build up. In the management consultancy business, for example, the position has changed in two years from a zero interest in BS 5750 approval for themselves (consultants were of course often happy to recommend that their clients went for BS 5750) to many consultancies scrambling for registration as fast as possible.

Seeking BS 5750 because you have to is bound to be seen in a negative way. If a company adopts the Standard reluctantly, because customers demand it, the chances are that the full benefits of a quality system will not be obtained. However, the coin is two-sided; if existing customers demand BS 5750, it is very likely that new business will come in as a result of successful registration. At its simplest, this will mean orders from customers who have already adopted a BS 5750-only supplier policy and this may enable a small company to make the leap from supplying only correspondingly small customers to blue chip business. BS 5750 may bring in not only more, but a different class of business and herald a period of rapid growth. A furniture manufacturer, for whom one of the authors acted as a consultant, had for years tried to supply products to the DHSS, but without success. With BS 5750 approval, the company was accepted on the approved supplier list and within a year obtained orders which doubled turnover. The costs of BS 5750, therefore, in this case, were demonstrably recovered in less than a year and this is by no means unusual. Sadly, such examples are reported less often than when things go wrong – 'BS 5750 shock-horror' stories in the trade press.

Extra business through BS 5750 does not just come from large customers with a formal requirement that suppliers are approved to the Standard. BS 5750 almost always enhances the quality standing of company and since all buyers seek quality, there is a positive business gain. If in an industry few competitors have (as yet) sought BS 5750, those which have will be positively differentiated as quality leaders. In your own industry you may be the first to be registered and this offers a major marketing opportunity, but one that should be rapidly exploited as others will soon catch up. In general, the benefits of BS 5750 will only be reaped if a company actively promotes its new status. Gaining BS 5750 will take money and effort and, once gained, should be a central part of the marketing effort including mentions in PR, advertising, and direct mail to customers and should be built into proposals and quotations.

Another source of additional business through BS 5750 registration is from companies in other parts of the European single market and overseas generally. An internationally recognised quality standard reduces barriers. When buying from a distant supplier, quality can be an especially serious concern. Often, much depends on perceptions of the ability of a supplier to meet requirements and this is inevitably uncertain where the supplier is from another country. Adherence to a known quality standard helps to reduce these problems. Also, although other countries are behind the UK in the number of companies registered to a national standard, the momentum is increasing. Just as in the UK large companies are starting to adopt a BS 5750-only supply policy, their counterparts in Germany, France and Italy are likewise insisting that suppliers can demonstrate an effective quality system. As we explained in chapter 2, assessment for BS 5750 automatically confers approval to the international ISO 9000 series of standards which in all countries is a recognised equivalent of the local national standard for quality systems. BS 5750, therefore, potentially offers increased international business.

As we stated earlier, this chapter covers the specific benefits of BS 5750 rather than quality systems generally. The external benefits of BS 5750 cannot, though, be practically separated from the general benefits of a quality system. As we will argue shortly, BS 5750 helps cement a quality system; it helps to ensure the system works well. An effective quality system will produce quality improvements and improved quality will bring in business. In the end, this is by far the most important long-term external benefit from BS 5750.

Before moving to the internal benefits there is one last point to make: BS 5750 can only bring external benefits if customers understand what the Standard means. By and large, in business-to-business markets (where the customer is another company or organisation rather than a private individual) BS 5750 is understood even if only vaguely. Outside business-to-business markets, among the general public, BS 5750 is not known and in such 'retail' level markets the external benefits of having the Standard may be slight. A grocer does not need to worry that customers will stop dealing with him if he cannot display a BS 5750 certificate at the front of the shop. Similarly, if he does display it, the extra customer pull will probably be insignificant (although some retail products do display the BS 5750 mark, eg one of the authors saw it (wrongly) on kitchen cabinets, but it had no obvious impact on would-be customers). However, the range of 'retail' only businesses which have chosen to seek BS 5750 is surprising, eg doctors, dentists and schools. Generally, it will probably be the internal rather than external benefits which have been sought, but it is possible that even where the customers have a low awareness of BS 5750 as such, the award of it can be communicated and understood as a symbol of commitment to quality. The ordinary consumer is as much concerned to buy 'quality' as the most technical of industrial buyers.

Now to the internal benefits of BS 5750. The general internal benefits of a quality system all relate to getting it right first time – reducing scrap and reworking, less down-time in tight schedules and preventing the human frustration of someone else not meeting requirements. The improvements and savings of this sort can be a massive benefit to a business, but can be obtained only if the quality system is effective. BS 5750 is a standard for effective systems.

Firstly, it is a symbol of commitment. Preparing a company for BS 5750 is not a trivial matter, as we will demonstrate in the remainder of the book. It inevitably has a significant cost. As well, BS 5750 involves having outside assessors visit the company and establish that the quality system is being followed in full. A company seeking BS 5750, therefore, cannot just pay lip-service to quality; if it does, it will fail the assessment. Also, the assessment for BS 5750 involves the whole company and all employees. Of necessity, therefore, the process of seeking BS 5750 implies important messages for all, eg:

- Quality is everyone's concern.
- We are all committed to the quality system.
- If it doesn't work we will change it – not ignore it.

This applies to not only the shop floor, but also the managers – right up to the top. This is important, because in some small companies quality problems can arise as much through the boss ignoring procedures as employees doing so.

Fine but I wanted it green . . .

Tideswell Controls produced bespoke air conditioning units. With so many possible permutations in design, it was vital that customers' requirements were precisely defined. The owner of the company, Paul, had designed a detailed checklist to make sure every possible requirement was covered and specified. This was filled in by the salesman, went to the design room and was used as a check on the shop floor. Paul was no tyrant, but a salesman only forgot to complete the customer requirement form once.

Paul was usually involved in larger orders and a few were handled only by him. He was very pleased when he won an order for a major new factory in Derby. With 33 units, it was the largest single order ever. Paul discussed all the details with the customer and personally briefed both the design team and the production managers. Of course, he did not complete a customer design form – he never did. There was no need; after all, he designed the form and knew all the contents by heart.

When the order was nearly ready, the customer was invited to visit Tideswell to see some of the equipment. The first five units were displayed in reception with the dark blue stove enamel mirror-polished.

After a brief glance the customer frowned. 'Yes, they seem fine Paul, but you must know I wanted them green. You have been round our other factory and seen that all our gear is a standard green. No way can we have just the control boxes blue.'

Repainting was not a simple matter. At the very least the whole units would have to be dis-assembled. 'Well don't look at me, Paul,' said the finishing room manager. 'Blue is our standard and blue it is unless something different is specified on the form.'

With BS 5750 everyone, including Paul, would be required to follow the contract review part of the quality system. Just because he is the boss and designed the system, Paul is not excused from following the procedures. Similarly, all other members of the staff are expected to follow the system. It is not just the boss that insists; it is the system.

Telling The Shopfloor

Andrew was seen as the rising star of the business. Single-handed, he not only brought in the best business, but his design work was first-class. His shortcomings? Well, like many really bright people he could be a tiny bit arrogant or perhaps he just didn't realise that not everybody was as quick on the uptake as himself. The quality system required that written job instructions should be passed to the workroom. Andrew prepared instructions but they were a bit short on detail and he could be offhand if asked to explain more fully. 'Just get on with it, Anne', he would tell the workroom manager. Sometime this led to problems and faults but Anne, who held the designers in awe, just stayed behind and put things right.

Because the quality system had been developed to BS 5750, internal quality audits were routine. An instance of Andrew's curt instructions leading to faults was identified and reported to the quality manager (who was also a senior director). A corrective action was duly issued and Andrew was given the task of investigating the problem. He was forced to recognise that the deficiency was his and in his report owned up to the mistake.

However, the quality manager was not satisfied and called Andrew in.

'You have identified the problem, Andrew, but in honesty I am sure that Anne had recognised this already. The question is, how do we stop it happening again? Don't tell me you will just try harder, either.'

Eventually it was agreed that the quality system should be changed and any deficient work instructions returned to the author for amendment before work started.

*   *   *

Andrew, even with the best of intentions, soon lapsed and again sent instructions lacking clear details. Anne now returned them for correction. Andrew hated it, but could not blame Anne.

'It's this BS 5750. You can't get away with anything now,' he complained, as he sat down to a late dinner at home. 'In future, I will just have to spend more time on these silly instructions and get them right.'

The depersonalisation aspect of BS 5750 also helps other personnel problems. Problems in performance can be judged not only in the opinion of a manager, but against a standard which is seen to be fair and objective. Performance problems can also be taken out of a formal hierarchy and addressed across the business.

Incidently, the quality system would have allowed Anne to raise a corrective action to deal with the problem; the system provided a mechanism for real problems to be addressed without it becoming a personal issue of Anne versus Andrew.

A BS 5750 quality system is also a tool of management control. Without a formalised set of procedures, management control is just a matter of bosses telling and workers jumping. At worst, requirements are seen as personal whims which are imposed from above without any known reason. They may be followed, but with an ill grace. More often time is spent in sabotaging a tyrannical régime. A formalised system is a big improvement. Now things are done because they are in the book and everyone knows what is required of them. Still some of the requirements are felt to be onerous and there at the management's whim rather than for good reason. Arbitrariness is reduced, but it is still present.

A quality system assessed to BS 5750 is, however, legitimised. The requirements of the system are now seen not as managers' whims, but as necessary to comply with a recognised standard. Who can now argue against the system? Furthermore, although in this way BS 5750 systems are a tool of management control, they encourage rational and benign systems. In particular, active and positive participation is encouraged through the requirements for controlled change procedures. If the system is to work, all must understand its purpose of quality maximisation and be encouraged to participate fully in making changes to solve problems.

A BS 5750 system has to incorporate the triad of audit, corrective action and management review shown in chapter 2. This is a powerful problem-solving tool. A further internal benefit of BS 5750 is, therefore, that problems have to be faced up to and solved. In any business or other organisation there is a tendency to mend and make do and concentrate on the short term. Come what may, we have to get the product out and the money in (or the equivalent in a non-business environment). But by keeping our noses to the grindstone, our vision is reduced to the short term. We never lift up our heads and take a longer-term view and before we know it, our twenty years at the business is twenty years of repeating the same mistakes. A quality system designed to meet the requirements of BS 5750 forces us to take a longer view through the need to identify problems and solve them – and keep on solving them until we have got them near right.

Finally, a further internal benefit is that a BS 5750 quality system is a framework for the successful growth of a small company. A company may start as little more than a one-man band. Quality is high because the owner is committed to his success, and not only oversees everything but pretty well does everything. As success comes, staff are brought in, but initially they are just helpers working under the constant personal supervision of the owner. However, even with the greatest commitment and the longest of days the owner starts to find that physically he cannot be everywhere at once. If he is out getting in the orders, the workers back at base have to be left to their own devices. Sooner or later this leads to a crisis. Quality is slipping and the workers are being blamed for a lack of commitment. Perhaps the answer is to bring in some better qualified staff, but who wants to work for someone who is known to be never satisfied?

At the right time, the answer to controlling growth is to set up a quality system and BS 5750 provides a standard which, if met, will ensure the system is effective and can grow with the business. The company is still individual, with the stamp of the founder, but staff now have their own space. Their participation makes quality a company-wide concern and no longer dependent just on the owner's driving energy. With everyone working to a common 'song-sheet' the owner can afford to focus energy where his or her interests and skills really lie. Furthermore, the system allows new staff to slot in, work to the best of their talents and give their own commitment to quality. In turn, this attracts a higher quality of staff and all these factors come together to both allow successful growth and stimulate it. Of course, over time the quality system has to change to meet the new circumstances and conditions of the company, but in a system designed to meet BS 5750 this dynamic element is built in.

THE DRAWBACKS

There are potential drawbacks to BS 5750 and these should be faced before any decision is made to implement a system. There are first and foremost the costs to be considered. However, costs have to be set against benefits. At the end of this chapter we suggest how the calculation might be done and for the moment will leave this subject aside.

A company moving from a situation of no formal quality system to implementing one that meets BS 5750 will face a culture shock, and this will be particularly acute in small companies with management issues largely the preserve of the owner. As we discussed, a major internal benefit of BS 5750 is that all, from the top down, have to be committed to the system and be willing to follow the procedures even when it feels uncomfortable. The greatest change may be faced by the boss; he perhaps must change from being an absolute ruler to a constitutional monarch. He is as bound by the rules as the office junior. In a rather larger organisation the same problem may be faced by the whole management layer. They can no longer be 'robber barons' sovereign in their own fiefdoms. If you the reader, as is likely, are the owner of a small company and are used to having everything your own way, how will you cope when the foreman raises a corrective action pointing out a problem which has come from your desk? Can you take this? If not, BS 5750 is not for you.

Bureaucracy is often seen as the major drawback to BS 5750. Some, wrongly, see a BS 5750 system as the sum of its forms and nothing else. It has to be accepted that there is some truth in this charge. A requirement of the Standard is record-keeping, eg *4.16 Quality Records,* and generally this involves forms. However, it is difficult to imagine an operating process producing consistently high quality without records of some sort being kept. Often these are kept accurately but in 'little black books' known to only a few people and if they are away, the records lapse. Worse, the record-keeping is spasmodic and haphazard. If records are needed, they should be accurate and complete. This will be best achieved if the forms are well designed and there is an auditing system to check that recording is done. If the records serve no useful purpose, they should be neither made nor kept. The process of designing a quality system for BS 5750 will involve a critical review of existing records. Quite likely, some records will be scrapped as new ones are introduced. It is even possible that the total record-keeping activity declines. Certainly a BS 5750 system can result in a massive explosion of form-filling, but if this is the case there are problems in the system design. The Standard does not require that any specific forms are kept as part of the system – it cannot, because it is only a standard against which individual systems are measured (see 'The fourth copy' case opposite).

The forms (or other equivalent records such as computer files) in your own system should be essential to the successful operation of your own process and if not, they should be scrapped. Arguably, periodic critical review of all forms ought to be built into the system.

Another possible drawback of BS 5750 is that it can degenerate into a legalistic game. At worst, the quality system can be designed purely to 'get through' BS 5750 without any regard to seeking a real improvement in quality.

DO YOU WANT BS 5750? 55

The fourth copy

The consultant was reviewing the working of the company's purchasing system and asked to see the current order forms. They came in pads of four: a top sheet and three carbonless copies.

'How is each copy used?', asked the consultant.

'The top copy goes to the supplier, of course. The second goes to the department which will receive the order and the third in the ordering file.'

'And the fourth copy?'

'Oh it goes to Cath.'

A little later, the consultant asked Cath where she kept her copy of the order form.

'Well I haven't any room to file my copy. When they start to build up, I throw them away.'

Much ingenuity is given to fitting the operating process to the system rather than vice versa – this job is a one-off and needs methods that are outside the system, but with a bit of tweaking we can make it look right in the records. These problems only arise because either the motive for seeking BS 5750 is wrong or because insufficient thought or time has been allocated to designing the system. Maybe the impetus to BS 5750 was the insistence of a major customer, but it is better (and probably not much more expensive) to go the whole way, design an effective system and reap all the benefits. Turn an imposed burden into a real vehicle for positive change.

If the system does not match the needs of the business, if bending the rules is constant, the system was badly designed in the first place and whose fault is that? Not BSI; the Standard gives enormous flexibility for designing a system to match almost any situation. You can perhaps put some of the blame on the consultant who designed large chunks of it, but who left him to his own devices in the first place? Consultants can play an invaluable role, but it is a supportive one. It is your responsibility to match a BS 5750 system to your individual needs. If you find it does not work, change it. If you do not, you will lose most of the benefits and in the longer run, BS 5750 approval. A poorly designed system cannot be adhered to and the independent assessors will start to find so many non-compliancies that registration will be withdrawn.

This leads to a final drawback to consider. Outside assessors are a real nuisance. They take up your time, frighten the staff and generally poke their noses into your business. Worse still you have to pay them. All this is true. However, a system such as BS 5750 requires independent third party assessment and if you really cannot accept this, forget the whole thing. Also, inspection by an independent third party assessor may be preferable to successive waves of customers examining the procedures (and perhaps also looking for ways of shaving your price). Finally, why should you have anything to hide from the assessors? You chose the firm to act as assessors and the system is yours; all they are doing is checking that you are doing the things which you say should be done. True, the assessors have to make sure your system matches the requirements of the Standard, but once over that hurdle the only yardsticks they can judge you against are ones that you set.

THE RELEVANCE OF BS 5750

A quite common view of BS 5750 is that it is a good thing in general and for other companies. Perhaps a very good thing for our suppliers, but not for us. Or our business is unique and BS 5750 was not written to meet the needs of our very specialised operation. Also, we have nothing in common with the sort of engineering operation that BSI appears to have had in mind.

The authors in their respective careers as consultants have only ever met businesses which (according to their owners or managers) are unique, special and completely unintelligible to anyone who has not spent a lifetime of initiation into the mysteries of the crafts. ('You mean to say you have no experience of making burnished left-hand gimlets with eccentric grommets . . .?') All true, but equally all businesses are also the same. At the very least, they all have inputs, do something with whatever comes into the business and provide outputs to customers whose needs must be satisfied if the business is to thrive.

Turning back to Figure 2.1 in chapter 2, it will be recalled that we considered the core of BS 5750 requirements address the operating process and that the other requirements have a supportive (but vital) role. Any operating process can be characterised as a sequence of input–process–output. Implementation of a quality system to meet BS 5750 standards seeks to ensure that the inputs are to a specified standard (eg through the purchasing process), that the process itself is controlled and that the output is monitored for conformity to requirements.

Figure 3.1 The operating process

It is difficult to think of a business which does not fit the pattern of input–process–output. Figure 3.2 gives three examples with particular inputs, processes and outputs described. The examples move from a business which might find the language of the Standard familiar (forging) through to one far removed from the engineering industry. All, however, have inputs–process–outputs and the relevant requirements of BS 5750 can be applied to maximising the quality in each of the three stages of the operating process.

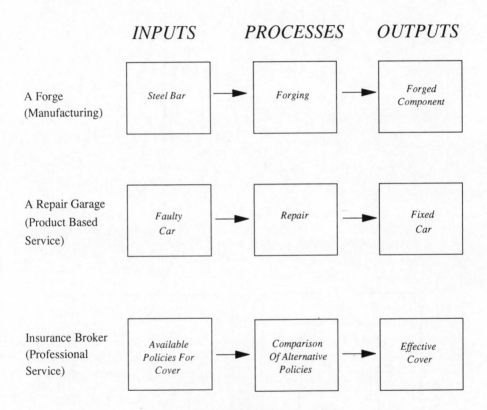

Figure 3.2 Operating processes

Of course, complex businesses have a multitude of input–process–output sequences, but given analysis time this complexity can be adequately represented and the application of BS 5750 will become easier to grasp.

As we have accepted, all businesses are unique and therefore their quality systems will be unique. Even within one industry the quality systems will vary widely to meet the differences in the inputs, the way the processes are carried

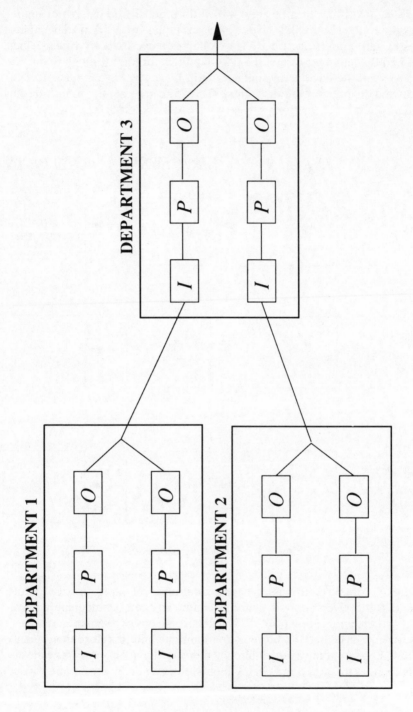

Figure 3.3 Complex operating process

out and the variety of outputs. However, all companies will be pursuing the same quality goal through implementing their own systems, the adequacy of which can be measured against the requirements of BS 5750.

Returning again to Figure 2.1 in chapter 2; if we accept that the requirements of the Standard contained within the operating process box can be applied to all businesses because they address input–process–output sequences, then the universal application of the support activities is even easier to recognise. At least two of the three quality resources – purchasing and training – exist in all businesses and in most there is a need to control inspection, measuring and monitoring equipment. The requirements we have classified as quality records and as quality system control are those which arise from the quality system itself and are generally autonomous of the actual business activity carried out.

All this is a theoretical argument for the universal application of BS 5750. There is, in addition, the empirical evidence of the very wide range of organisations which are now registered for the Standard. In fact it is now hard to find any groupings of businesses which do not include BS 5750 firms. Moreover, interest is not confined to commercial businesses. Other types of organisation known to be either registered or, at the time of writing, considering BS 5750, include: central and local Government departments, doctors and health bodies, schools and a police force (the Notting Hill station of the Metropolitan Police were reported in the *Independent* (9 April 1992) to be asking Scotland Yard for the go-ahead to seek BS 5750).

A final point before moving from the relevance of BS 5750, is that while in principle any organisation can realistically seek to be BS 5750 approved, some will find the process easier than others. Particular problems may be faced in very small companies (one-man bands cannot carry out their own auditing, but might consider setting up co-operative schemes with similar but complementary businesses); very large companies (because of the complexity); or in any business where the management lacks the time for strategic planning – but then strategy development is an activity of any successful management team.

THE COSTS

Because variations are likely to be so large between organisations, no general figures can be given for the net costs of BS 5750. There is also the problem that figures estimated at the time will become outdated. Estimates have to be made in each and every specific case. Table 3.1 provides a costing framework and takes into account the value of the gains from BS 5750 as well as the costs entailed. Clearly, it is necessary to decide in any such costing exercise what time period is to be considered. Some of the associated costs are one-off (eg consultancy and initial assessment) whilst others are ongoing. The gains are all generally ongoing.

Table 3.1 *Costing BS 5750*

Costs		Gains	
	£		£
Assessment costs	...	Value of retained business	...
Consultancy and training costs	...	Value of additional business	...
Staff time costs	...	Value added to products	...
Marketing and similar costs	...	Efficiency savings	...
		Government grants etc	...

Assessment costs are the charges made by the independent third party assessors (see chapter 11) for both initial assessment and ongoing surveillance (eg once or twice a year). Charges will be based on factors including the nature and complexity of the operation, the number of employees and whether more than one site is involved. As will be described later (chapter 11), proposals and quotations from several potential assessors should be sought before signing up; the costs can vary widely. In 1992, a professional service business with 60 employees was charged £5,500 for a three-year programme of assessment and surveillance (averaging under £2,000 per annum, although the first year's payment was higher). These figures are given as illustrations only, but for a smaller company, on one site and with under a hundred employees, the assessment costs are unlikely to be more than the cost of one modest company car.

Probably most organisations seeking BS 5750 will decide to buy-in expertise either through the services of a consultant or through outside training programmes. In either case the costs involved will depend on the scale of input sought. In 1992 a smaller firm of consultants offering expertise in quality systems and BS 5750 implementation could be charging at the rate of £400 to £500 per man-day. A full programme of implementation might entail 15 – 20 man-days and, therefore, a total cost at 1992 price levels of £6,000 to £10,000. However, the consultant input might be less (or more) and as will be mentioned shortly, government grants can offset some of these costs. Charges for outside training seminars in 1992 averaged £100–£200 per delegate-day for 'open' courses, ie those not tailored to the needs of a specific organisation.

Both consultancy and training will be largely one-off and initial although continuous training, or at least assessment of training needs, is a requirement of BS 5750.

The costs of staff time cover the extensive design and initial setting-up work; the chapters in Part Two should help the reader make realistic calculations. In smaller firms the total of such time might be of the order of a hundred man-days and the cost would depend on whatever valuation is put on the time of the staff involved (not only based on their remuneration package, but also taking into account any losses from not carrying out other tasks). There is also an ongoing staff cost (eg the time involved in auditing, corrective actions and management reviews, as well as the continuous administration of the quality system). In smaller companies this time may be very difficult to separate from general management activities, while in larger companies specific quality staff may have to be recruited. Again, an informed estimate has to be made in each and every individual case.

As we mentioned earlier, a firm gaining BS 5750 must promote its newly accredited quality system and this will involve some specific marketing costs. Perhaps the letterhead and sales literature will need reprinting, or a BS 5750 launch may entail the planning of special activities. However, on an ongoing basis the extra costs are probably small since a given level of marketing would be carried out in any case. Finally, the system may involve printing costs for documents and material directly connected with the quality system.

On the gains side of the costing, there is firstly the ongoing value of retained business – that which might be eventually lost through not having BS 5750. We suggest that to estimate this figure the reader takes perhaps the ten largest customers and puts against each a probability, out of ten, that the company concerned will insist on BS 5750 within, say, two years. This probability fraction can then be applied to the annual value of each customer and the total of 'business at risk' calculated. It is not uncommon for this calculation to arrive at a figure greater than the estimated costs of a BS 5750 system.

The figure for gains from additional business obtained as a result of BS 5750 is perhaps the hardest calculation of all. We do not know where this might come from; we may as yet have never met the customer. All we can suggest is taking a modest assumption of additional business over and above the 'normal' annual growth of a company's turnover – if this is 10 per cent a year, another 1 per cent might be a sensible 'guesstimate'.

An effective quality system will make the product (or service) better in the eyes of the customer. Buyers in any market will often pay more for something that is better because it has added value. BS 5750 and the successful implementation of the quality system, therefore, may offer some potential for increasing prices. Even a 1 per cent price rise is straight on to profit and can be set against the costs of BS 5750 set-up and operation.

Also, there are the gains of efficiency savings. An effective quality system increases the chances of getting things right first time and reduces scrapping or reworking levels which have a calculable cost. Again, the reader should be able to make a conservative valuation of such savings.

Finally, at the time of writing the Government has grant schemes available to at least smaller companies setting up new quality systems. For example, under the DTI's Enterprise Initiative programme approved companies in certain areas can receive a grant for up to two-thirds of the costs of a 15-day consultancy programme. Similarly, some Training and Enterprise Councils offer low-cost, quality system training. Contact with these bodies, or other public agencies (see Appendix 2), is clearly worthwhile to establish what assistance is currently on offer – the terms and scope of the schemes vary year to year.

4   HOW TO GET BS 5750 – AN OVERVIEW

Design and implement a quality system, meeting the requirements of the Standard, have a successful assessment completed by a suitable assessor body and you then have BS 5750. That is all. This chapter provides an overview of the major steps involved in the process, with the full details covered in chapters 5 – 12 of Part Two.

Part Two provides an action plan for an organisation to implement BS 5750 entirely through its own resources. However, few businesses are likely to carry out all the work themselves. The possible role of consultants and other forms of outside assistance is covered in the latter part of this chapter.

BS 5750: THE MAJOR STEPS

Figure 4.1 represents the major steps to BS 5750. Chapter references to Part Two are provided; *Project Planning*, for example, is covered in detail in chapter 5. The activities in the centre block of the figure follow logically in sequence and correspond to the order of the chapters of Part Two. Two steps, however, *Contact And Select Assessors* and *Select And Train Internal Audit Team*, can be taken at points other than as illustrated in the figure.

Decision And Commitment

Whatever else is needed to implement BS 5750, commitment must come first. At least the senior management of the organisation must believe that BS 5750 is a worthwhile goal and should clearly understand both the major benefits (as discussed in chapter 3) and the extent of the considerable work involved. If there are any major doubts, the project is better postponed until these are resolved. Nor is it enough that the senior management are committed; all staff will be involved and should understand the benefits for both the company and

63

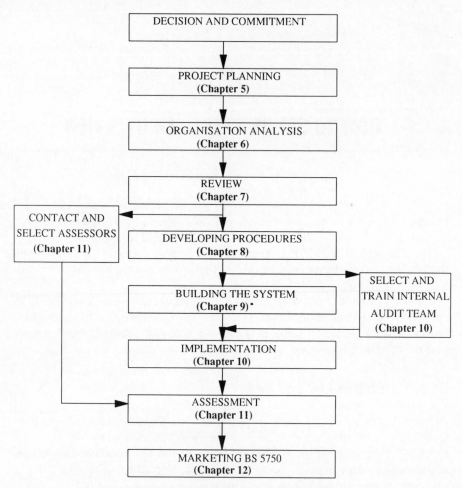

Figure 4.1 BS 5750: the major steps

themselves individually. Also, they should be briefed on how they will be involved in setting up a quality system and working it. A bridge between the commitment of the senior management and the rest of the staff is a formal *quality policy*.

As we will describe later, the formal documentation requirements of BS 5750 include a quality policy. Typically, this is a short statement which commits the organisation to implementing a quality system to meet the requirements of BS 5750 and requires the involvement of all staff in the system. Figure 4.2 gives an example of a quality policy; the wording can be adapted to meet the needs and house-style of a particular organisation.

C OMPANY Q UALITY P OLICY

It is the policy of Business & Market Research plc to provide the highest quality
of service to clients.

The Company is a commercial business operating in a competitive market. The
pursuit of the highest quality of service to clients is as essential to the long term
growth and survival of the business as cost control and optimum pricing.

In order to ensure that all work is carried out in a manner which provides the highest
quality of service to clients, the Company has put into effect the Quality System.
This complies with the requirements of BS 5750 Part 1: 1987/ISO 9001.
The Quality Manual defines this system and the work procedures entailed.

All staff are required:

To be completely familiar with and understand all procedures of the Quality System
relevant to their own work for the Company.

To follow and comply with the requirements of all such procedures.

This policy statement has been adopted by a resolution of the Board of Directors
dated October 7th 1991.

Peter Jackson, Director

Figure 4.2 Specimen quality policy

In a company managed through regular board meetings, the quality policy may be formally adopted by resolution and then suitably displayed. However, it is essential that all staff are at this point told what the policy means and how they will be involved. How this is done will depend on the size and structure of the organisation. Generally, however, the best method is one or more short meetings led by the 'boss', who fleshes out the policy and discusses why it has been adopted and what will happen next.

The decision to go for BS 5750 also involves a choice of which Part – in most cases either Part 1, involving design, or Part 2, excluding design. Generally, the choice will be clear-cut; the business either involves a design element as part of its contracts or it does not and Part 1 or 2 will be selected accordingly (see chapter 2). In theory, a business with a design function may tactically choose to exclude this activity and register for Part 2 only, but some key marketing advantages of BS 5750 could be lost (see chapter 12 for further discussion of this point). Moreover, in nearly all situations the *extra* effort required to achieve Part 1 rather than Part 2 will not be enormous and in either case BS 5750 will be a major project.

In a few cases, the choice between Part 1 and Part 2 will be at the outset uncertain. If this is the situation the decision can be deferred until the *Organisational Analysis* has been completed.

A related decision will be whether to seek BS 5750 registration for the whole organisation or only some departments, branches or units. This book is primarily written with the smaller company in mind and in most cases the organisation will not be complex enough for this question to arise. In larger businesses there may be an argument for introducing BS 5750 in part of the organisation as a pilot and then rolling out. Unless, however, the pilot department is relatively self-contained, many of the external and marketing advantages of registration will not be reaped immediately (again, see chapter 12).

Project Planning

In virtually all companies the process of gaining BS 5750 will be a major project, possibly the largest ever undertaken. Much will depend on the choice of an effective project leader and his supporting team. A timetable is needed as part of the plan, otherwise there will be a tendency for completion to be ever-delayed. Significant costs will be entailed and this should be budgeted. All these and other elements of project planning are discussed in chapter 5. Another aspect of project planning is the use of outside assistance; consultants or others. This is the subject of the latter part of this present chapter.

Organisation Analysis

Managers of smaller companies may be surprised that they need to carry out an analysis of their own organisation; a 'family tree' diagram of the company is usually available. However, we mean a rather more fundamental analysis than this and one that probably involves looking at the business in a new way. Chapter 6 describes in detail what is required and shows how this type of analysis is needed to relate the particular organisation to the requirements of BS 5750.

Review

The most fundamental part of an effective quality system is the *Quality Procedures:* the working methods to be followed to maximise quality. Having carried out an organisation analysis, the review (chapter 7) is undertaken to determine what procedures are required. In at least some areas of the business, it is quite likely that adequate procedures are in place and used (they may not be recognised as procedures). It is unlikely, however, that they will be sufficiently documented to meet the requirements of the Standard, but the work involved in writing up an effective and adequate existing procedure is fairly small. In other areas a review will show that adequate procedures are not in place. The outcome of the review will therefore be a list of required procedures; either new ones or those which are in place, but need adequate documentation. Another outcome of the review is a set of policy statements on how each seperate clause of BS 5750 will be implemented in the particular company. These eventually form the core of the *Quality Manual.*

Selection Of Assessors

BS 5750 registration requires the assessment of a quality system and its implementation by third party assessors. Whilst BSI is the best-known accredited assessor body there are many others, although several specialise in particular businesses (eg Quality Scheme For Ready Mixed Concrete). In practice, most businesses seeking BS 5750 will be able to choose between at least three potential assessors and should regard the choice as an evaluation of alternate suppliers with normal commercial judgements applied. The assessment process is not a one-off event; after a company is successfully assessed initially, follow-up surveillance visits are carried out by the assessor body to make sure that the quality system continues to be followed, with a further full assessment often carried out after three years. There is, therefore, a continuing relationship with the assessor and this underlines the importance of the choice.

There is a 'lead time' in both making the choice and from 'signing up' to the actual assessment. The process of selection, therefore, can sensibly start about the time of the review. The details are, however, discussed towards the end of Part Two in chapter 11.

Developing Procedures

Developing the required procedures is the key and most onerous part of a BS 5750 project. A wide range of staff, not just the project team, should be involved. Chapter 8 describes in detail this part of this process and includes some illustrative specimen procedures.

Internal Audit Team

An essential part of implementing a successful quality policy is internal auditing. The team who will carry out this work should be selected and have initial training well before the new quality system is implemented. However, we conveniently discuss this subject as part of *Implementation* (chapter 10).

Building The System

The physical embodiment of a quality system is its documentation. (Do not fall into the error, though, of thinking that the quality system is only the documentation – the procedures, for example, have to be followed as well as written.) Figure 4.3 represents the documentation required as four distinct levels and arguably the critical one is the procedure manual. The policy statement (one page at most) will have been written at the outset of the project. The quality manual is also fairly short; its purpose is to relate a company's quality system to the requirements of the Standard and most of the work required will arise out of the review (chapter 7). The bottom layer of documentation is the records kept of the operation of the system and the master copies of any forms or other recording media will be included in the procedure manual.

Chapter 9 describes how a complete quality system can be produced and suggests appropriate layout formats. An important aspect of documentation which is also considered is meeting the Standard's requirements for document control.

Implementation

Once documented, the system has to be successfully implemented and operated for a period before an external assessment can be considered. Implementation can be either a one-off 'big bang' throughout the organisation, or rolled out department by department. There are good arguments for both approaches and these as well as other aspects of implementation are covered in chapter 10.

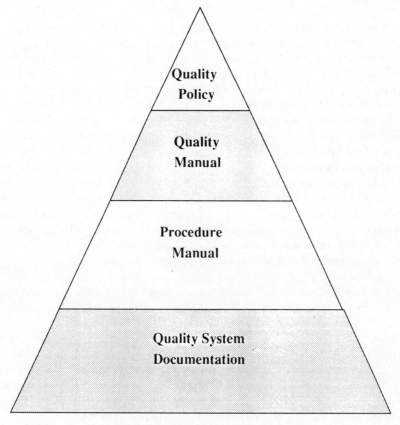

Figure 4.3 BS 5750: documentation

Assessment

The culmination of the project will be a successful first assessment. We describe in chapter 11 what happens during an assessment; it is a lot less stressful if you know what to expect and on what basis the assessment result will be favourable or otherwise. As we have already indicated, assessment is not a one-off affair and chapter 11 also covers follow-up surveillance visits.

Marketing BS 5750

Having gone to all the trouble and expense of becoming registered for BS 5750, every possible benefit should be wrung out of it. This needs a positive marketing programme – the subject of the final chapter (12) of Part Two.

CONSULTANTS AND OTHER OUTSIDE ASSISTANCE

The purpose of the this book is to provide a guide to 'DIY' implementation of BS 5750. However, in practice, only the very confident are likely to rely wholly on their own resources. At least *some* form of outside assistance will probably be sought. This certainly does not have to entail a large-scale consultancy programme; it may be far more cost-effective to buy in consultancy to guide critical stages of the project. Also there are other forms of outside assistance, besides consultancy, to consider. We will discuss the role and choice of consultants first and conclude the chapter with suggestions about other possible sources of outside assistance.

Consultants should not be used as an alternative to the work of internal staff. Their role is to advise and facilitate and not to substitute. Possibly they can be asked to prepare first drafts of some of the more standard parts of the quality system documentation: procedures covering the requirements of the Standard we termed *quality system control* in Figure 2.1 of chapter 2 and perhaps the *quality manual*, because these have at least a resemblance across companies. For the critical procedures of the *operating process* and *support activities* (as per Figure 2.1) as well as the analysis and review underlying them, it is vital that the client organisation's own staff have a primary input. The reason for this is that a consultant's work will be limited in duration; in all probability it will have finished well before the assessment and in any case it is not he who must *use* the procedures. If the staff of a company substantially design their own system, they will 'own' it and be responsible for its successful implementation. They can never blame anyone but themselves for the parts of the procedures which do not work (and some will not work first time, however carefully they are planned). Unfortunately there are consultants around who will offer to 'sit in a corner and write you a quality system'. Reject them out of hand.

Table 4.1 summarises the arguments for and against using consultants in setting up a quality system to meet BS 5750. The main argument for consultants is that they offer an expertise that few organisations seeking BS 5750 are likely to have in-house. If they are any good at all, they will know the requirements of the Standard inside out and have a broad base of experience in implementing it across a range of businesses. This is important, because the requirements of the Standard have to be interpreted in the context of particular businesses. As mentioned earlier, the Standard is not written in a language that a non-engineering businesses will find user-friendly and, particularly in the case of service activities, considerable creativity may be needed in finding ways the business can match up to some of the requirements. Arguably, it is not essential that the consultant has specific experience in your own business, since one of the benefits of a consultant can be the cross-fertilisation of ideas from different businesses making up his past client list. Finally on the 'pros' list is the fact that an experienced consultant can draw on available tried and tested quality system documentation. However, for both ethical and practical reasons (as mentioned above), do not expect a consultant to turn up with sets of manuals only requiring the name of your company to be word-processed in. At best, *some* examples may be adaptable.

Probably no one would quarrel with hiring a consultant if they came free of charge. The disadvantages are mainly to do with the costs. Consultants have nothing to sell but their time. At the time of writing, the charge basis may range from £25 per hour/£200 per day for a one-man firm up to £125 per hour/£1000 per day for a senior member of staff from a large practice. The going rate under DTI schemes, about £50 per hour/£400 per day, perhaps represents an average charge level. Such rates may appear expensive but remember they must cover all the consultant's costs, not just his wages, and are probably not much more than the *full* costs of the time of senior in-house staff. Also, a good consultant should save the client considerable time otherwise wasted in floundering around and mistakes. The old chestnut that a consultant is 'someone who borrows your watch to tell you the time' has some element of truth in it; consultants inevitably charge for the time they spend understanding your business, but in return they will offer the advantages of a fresh perspective on what to you are over-familiar activities. Furthermore, consultants may 'borrow your watch to tell you the time', but are you sure you would 'look at the time' yourself?

Once we have hired a consultant, we naturally seek to get the most out of him and if he is working in the right way he will be spurring on your own team – agreeing deadlines for each step of the project. Too often, purely internal projects become ever-postponed because of the pressure of day-to-day business. This brings up the final argument against the use of consultants: there is a danger that the work will end up being all done by him rather than with the essential internal involvement. In practice, even a half-competent consultant would not let this happen.

Table 4.1 *For and against using consultants*

For Consultants	Against Consultants
Know requirements of BS 5750	High charge rates
Implementation expertise	Pay them to learn your business
Cross fertilisation from other clients	Take over the project and you lose ownership
Have available material from other quality systems.	

Consultants generally offer full BS 5750 packages: programmes involving 10, 15, 20 or more days' work designed to steer the client from scratch up to an implemented quality system. The DTI-assisted scheme is based around 15 days (the most common input which is subsidised at the time of writing and generally the basis of a package taken up by supported companies). However, consultants can certainly be used more sparingly and most are willing to sell their time in units of single days. A consultant working on this basis might, for example, be asked to give initial overall guidance (say, one day), participate in the organisation analysis and review (three days) and review the system immediately prior to implementation (one day). In this way, at a cost of the charges made for five consultant days, an outside perspective is brought in and there is an independent judgement made of the match between System and Standard before formal assessment. Mixing and matching the input of consultants with other forms of outside assistance can also be considered. For example, local Training And Enterprise Councils (TECs) have sponsored self-help 'clubs' of local small businesses seeking BS 5750 with the costs of consultants shared by the whole group.

Consultants come in various forms. The only really vital difference is between good ones and bad ones and unfortunately this aspect is the hardest to judge beforehand. Some suggestions for minimising a poor choice are provided shortly. In size, the range is from one-man bands of which, in this field, there are many, though medium-sized practices up to multinational groups. Without a doubt, one-man bands can offer an excellent and cost-effective service. Moreover there is no question of a smooth 'front man' selling-in and leaving the actual work to a callow youth; this can happen with larger practices. Unfortunately, the quality of one-man bands varies enormously and while some are excellent, others range from the barely competent to the outright fraudulent. The risks of a bad service are thus arguably higher than with a larger consultancy. Another problem with one-man bands is that they have no additional resources to draw on; the consultant may be first-class, but you are in trouble if he goes down with a long-term illness. Also, he cannot bring in additional advice. Although even with a larger consultancy the work may be largely carried out by a single individual, other staff are available for support and perhaps to finally vet the completed quality system before implementation.

Another difference between consultancies is specialisation. Some specialise in quality or even BS 5750 implementation, while others are generalists. The largest practices may offer a quality team or unit as part of a range of specialisations. On the whole we consider that specialists have more to offer; after all, you are seeking expertise in BS 5750. However, there is one good argument for a generalist; with a broad experience the consultant may be able to diagnose business problems to the side of a strict quality approach and therefore make a greater overall contribution to your business.

The process of selecting a consultant starts with drawing up a shortlist of available consultants who apparently have something useful to offer. Possible sources of this list are suggested below.

DTI

Even if you already have a shortlist of possible consultants, an approach to the DTI or their major contractors for quality consultancy, Salford University Business Services Limited (SUBSL) and Production Engineering Research Association (PERA), is strongly recommended. Quite apart from any lists of consultants they may be able to offer, the DTI, at the time of writing, makes available significant grants towards the cost of quality consultancy (up to two-thirds of the cost of a 15-day project). However, the rules of the scheme are quite complex and alter. It is better for an interested reader to make direct contact with the DTI or their contractors than rely on any guidance we may offer. Another advantage of an approach to these bodies is that any consultant suggested is likely to be at least minimally competent.

TECs

Local Training And Enterprise Councils are another type of quasi-official body which may provide lists of consultants. If you are not already in contact with the TEC for your area, look them up in the local phone book.

Association Of Quality Management Consultants

Most specialist quality consultancies will belong to this body, which may make available lists of suitable firms. Obviously they must be even-handed to all their members and cannot recommend one over another.

Management Consultancy Association

This is a more broadly based body and may also be worth approaching.

Trade Associations

The trade association for your own type of business should always be approached. Formally or otherwise, they may be able to give the names of quality consultants with experience of your own type of business. Moreover, for other reasons, it is worth learning at an early stage what involvement, if any, the trade association has had with BS 5750 (see chapter 5). Similarly, the trade press may well mention firms in your industry who have recently gained BS 5750; you could approach them to learn of their experience with consultants. Local chambers of commerce may be a similar potential source.

The contact addresses for the DTI, DTI contractors and the consultancy associations are provided in Appendix 2.

Making the right choice

Having identified potentially suitable consultants, we recommend that you invite two or three to quote for carrying out the work – not a larger number since you would be wasting not only their time, but your own as well. You can expect the consultant to hold an initial meeting with you before preparing a formal proposal document. You should then read each proposal most carefully and establish:

- Do they demonstrate an understanding of the nature of your business and why you are pursuing BS 5750? A competent consultant should have picked this up at the initial meeting.
- Exactly what work are they proposing to carry out? Will they guide you through the process from start to finish or concentrate on specific activities?
- How do they propose to carry out the project? A recognised methodology is to carry out an initial audit (effectively, the review covered in chapter 7), identify where work is required and after this is complete, carry out a final audit to establish that the new quality system meets the Standard.
- A firm timetable and a fixed cost for the project; or at least spell out exactly how you will be charged.

If not covered in the written proposal, you should also establish who specifically will carry out the consultancy (assuming the firm is not a one-man band). Also, if you have not already done so, insist on meeting the individual consultant who will work on the project; this is vital. Whether the firm is large or small, most of the work will depend on one individual and you must feel comfortable working with him or her. You do not have to become bosom pals, but you must have confidence in their personal skills and feel able to communicate with them.

Undoubtedly, when considering a possible consultancy you will consider the experience they can offer in your own or a related business. In the authors' opinion, experience of a specific business is not essential, but there should be some symbiosis with the general type of business. If yours is a business service operation, a consultancy with experience of heavy engineering only is unlikely to be the best choice. Also, by all means ask for and take up references from past clients; of course, these will be the better rather than the worse examples of the consultancy's work, but they will at least indicate that some clients, at some time, have been satisfied. Finally, establish where the consultancy itself stands in relation to BS 5750. Have they taken or are they at least planning to take, their own medicine?

Training courses

The major form of outside assistance apart from consultants is training courses. These break down into open courses for anyone interested and tailored courses developed to meet the needs of a particular firm. The latter are essentially another type of consultancy and will not be discussed further.

Quite a few companies, as their core business, offer seminars in a range of business subjects including quality and BS 5750. At the time of writing charges are typically in the range of £100 to £200 per delegate day with one- or two-day courses common (the total amount at risk is, therefore, fairly modest). The more expensive courses do not necessarily offer a better content, but the seminar groups may be smaller and individual attention greater. Companies marketing this type of training usually advertise by direct mail and there is a good chance that you will have already received details (which you may have binned before you became interested in BS 5750).

Training courses in quality subjects are also organised through local TECs and these bodies should certainly be approached to learn what is on offer in your area. Grants or subsidised courses may also be available through TECs – another good reason for making contact.

Finally, trade associations should be contacted for details of training specific to a particular industry.

AN ACTION PLAN FOR BS 5750

We can now turn to an action plan for BS 5750.

The remaining chapters follow a sequence of steps to BS 5750. However, variations in the ordering of the activities may be appropriate to meet the needs of particular businesses. Some activities, for example, could be carried out in parallel rather than consecutively.

The key to success is thoughtful initial planning including timetabling, which is the subject of chapter 5. We urge readers though to read Part Two in total (OK, you can skip bits) before attempting to plan their own work – you cannot do this unless you understand everything that has to be covered in the project.

5 PROJECT PLANNING

Introducing BS 5750 will be a major project. In this chapter, the first in 'how to do it' Part Two, we show how the project can be planned effectively. Topics covered include: the project leader and his team, resources, initial research activities, timetabling and budgeting.

THE PROJECT LEADER AND HIS TEAM

The project leader's key task is to ensure that everything that has to happen between the formal start of the project and a successful assessment actually happens on time. In addition, the project manager will often carry out many of the tasks required as part of the project although strictly speaking most of them can be delegated, leaving the project leader to concentrate on managing. However, in most smaller businesses and organisations the project leader is inevitably involved in doing much of the detailed work as well. Similarly, the project leader does not have to be involved in managing the quality system once it is up and running; he does not have to become the *management representative*, in the terminology of the Standard. Again, in most smaller organisations the chief designer of the quality system has a continuing role in its operation; whether he likes it or not, he becomes the in-house quality guru.

The choice of leader

From our experience of working with BS 5750 project leaders, we can suggest some of the ideal qualities for leadership. We are very conscious, however, that many organisations do not have the luxury of making a choice between possible candidates, as there is only one in the running. Nevertheless we consider that the project leader ought to have at least some of the following strengths:

■ *Authority* In order to keep the project to a timetable, the project leader needs the authority to co-ordinate, if not command, staff and other resources. While the project is under way, business will undoubtedly have to be carried on as normal. When the involvement of staff in the project is required, some will plead the pressures of normal work as a reason for delay or side-stepping. The project leader needs the authority, if necessary, to demand the necessary input into the project, whatever the excuses. (He also needs the experience and wisdom to recognise when the project really must be put back to avoid real damage to the business.) In a smaller or medium-sized company the project leader, therefore, needs to be either at director level or only one step down. At this level he will have the necessary authority and the rest of the staff will understand his position.

- *Understanding of the business* The foundation of a successful BS 5750 project is applying the requirements of the Standard to the particular business. This book and other sources will provide knowledge of the requirements, but the leader must bring to the project an understanding of the particular business – how it is structured and organised, what is produced in the core processes and how these work. Probably, if the project leader is chosen on the basis of his authority, he will also have the necessary understanding of the business; he will quite likely have managed some critical functions for some time. Incidently, this need for an understanding of the core processes of the business may be a factor against choosing a project leader from the more specialist and service departments, including accounts and finance. The financial director, may be, on other grounds, the ideal candidate for the project, but if he is relatively remote from the work of the core processes he may face practical problems. The need for a close understanding of the business is also a very good reason for not allowing an outside consultant to take on the role of project manager. Even if a large-scale consultancy involvement is anticipated, the project management should remain firmly with internal staff – one of the project leader's key roles becomes choice of and close liaison with the consultants.

- *Project management experience* The project leader should have a track record of managing projects and preferably ones outside the day-to-day operation of the business. Such experience might include buying and commissioning major plant for the company, a re-organisation of the company structure or implementing a new computer system. In such 'extraordinary' projects the leader will have learnt how to rapidly build up expertise in a new field, how to co-ordinate others, how to improvise and what to do when things start going wrong; preventing a set-back becoming a catastrophe.

- *Adequate knowledge of and commitment to BS 5750* In very few businesses will this knowledge be present at the start of the project. So what we have in mind is the drive and enthusiasm to learn as much as necessary about the Standard. Such knowledge may come from reading this book or possibly attending training seminars, working with consultants or discussions with other businesses who have either gone through the process of gaining BS 5750 or are actively doing so.

■   *Sufficient available time*   Finally, the project manager must have sufficient available time to carry out the work. Since he will almost certainly have an existing and important role within the business, he will either have to off-load some of this routine (delegation of routine tasks may have long-term benefits to both the individual concerned and the company) or somehow squeeze in the extra time needed to manage the project. Probably, a bit of both. However, the leader's commitment to the project must be such that adequate time is found. What is adequate depends on the situation within the company – how much work is required to develop and implement a quality system – and the extent to which tasks can be delegated.

These cover the really key elements of an ideal project leader for BS 5750. The converse is who should not be given the job? In the authors' experience, the source of many problems experienced in gaining BS 5750 can be traced to making either 'dead elephants' or 'playful pups' project leaders.

A typical dead elephant is one of the founders of a business but perhaps the one who was always a 'number two'. He now has a certain status and is paid accordingly, but no one is quite sure what his responsibilities are. Such dead elephants may have an apparent authority because of their seniority within an organisation. However, they are no longer used to exercising it at a practical level. They may claim to have considerable knowledge of the business, but perhaps as it was ten years ago; they are now rather isolated from the day-to-day work of the business. They are also unfamiliar with rising to the demands of new challenges and may find it very difficult to understand the concepts of a quality system and the Standard. Above all, dead elephants have lost any capacity for urgency and action. Unfortunately, they often have something which no one else has: time. Dead elephants are often selected just because no one else can be spared from day-to-day activities. The problem of the dead elephant might, therefore, be re-stated: whoever has the time available to be project manager is unqualified for the job.

Playful pups have lots of enthusiasm; quite different from dead elephants. In fact, they demonstrate that the most dangerous people within an organisation are not the ignorant and idle but the ignorant and industrious. Typically, they are pups in the sense of being young and new to the organisation and very keen to prove their worth by master-minding BS 5750. However, they have a limited and partial understanding of the organisation's core processes (worse, they fail to recognise their limitations) and no real authority, but they may have the arrogance to alienate other staff from the whole thing. Also, playful pups have probably only ever played; they have no real experience of managing projects.

Once an effective project leader is selected, who else needs to be involved? As a general rule, the wider the involvement of staff throughout the organisation, the more effective the new quality system will be. Although in many organisations the project leader may be the only permanent member of the project team, other staff should be involved, as required, to carry out or advise on specific tasks. This is particularly the case with procedure writing. Unfortunately, beyond a certain point the delegation of project tasks to *ad hoc* groups of staff increases rather than diminishes the demands put on the project leader; he will have to spend time chasing up everyone involved and making sure their work is both within timetable and covers the requirement. The consultation process is, however, vital.

A few organisations may have an ideal project manager with adequate time available. This is a fortunate position to be in but in this case there is a danger of the project becoming a private affair. This must be resisted, because even though the project manager might be technically capable of developing an effective quality system, it will then belong to him rather than to the whole company. This will lead to acute problems at the implementation stage. Consultation throughout the organisation is needed not only to provide input into the design of the system, but, just as critically, to ensure that it is 'owned', and felt to be so owned, throughout the company. A department cannot resent following a set of procedures if it is closely involved in developing them. There is every chance they will resist the procedures that were designed without consultation.

At the project planning stage, therefore, it is essential to consider how consultation will be achieved. This might be at several levels. In a company managed through regular board meetings, the project manager could be asked to make a progress report at each meeting followed by a discussion. This would ensure that the functional heads are all involved in the project. Alongside, might be an *ad hoc* group of managers, below board level, meeting, say, weekly to discuss specific problems and progress. Additionally, staff from all levels might be intensively involved for a shorter period as procedures are developed for particular departments or functional areas. Some of these staff (and not necessarily the most senior in the hierarchy) may be asked to work together as procedure writers once this stage of the project is reached.

RESOURCES

Apart from staff time, a BS 5750 project is unlikely to require extensive resources. Records will have to be filed adequately, and documents and forms will eventually need printing, but these are unlikely to involve much more than a limited amount of additional stationery. More substantial expenditure could be involved if the review stage suggests an additional need for process (or associated measuring) equipment or inspection, but often core activities are only formalised rather than changed as a result of BS 5750. One resource, however, that should be seriously considered, if it is not already in use, is a word processor.

The documentation required for BS 5750 can be produced without a word processor, but the typing work is a lot harder and mistakes in the final documentation are more likely – and such mistakes can be expensive in the long run. In its preparation, many drafts of the documentation are likely to be needed before finalisation and without a word processor several complete re-types will be needed. Furthermore, once implemented, changes will be needed to be made to the documentation both to correct deficiencies that can only be identified through operating the system and to take account of changing circumstances (changes to the quality system will inevitably be ongoing and for ever). Again, a word processor is not essential but it is a tremendous help. Nor is the equipment now expensive; prices have over the last few years fallen drastically. At the present time, a complete package complete with a printer can be bought for well under £1,000 and even the technically illiterate can learn enough of a WP package to be able to use it with only a few hours' initial tuition. Moreover, few organisations will fail to gain some additional benefits from word processing over and above its BS 5750 application.

INITIAL RESEARCH

An early task of the project manager should be to carry out some initial research. Possibly some of this will have been already done before a commitment to BS 5750 was made. Areas we suggest should be covered in this initial research are as follows:

What is happening in the industry?

Almost certainly other organisations in your industry or field of activity will be involved in BS 5750, either considering it or already registered. Whilst each company's quality system is and should be unique, businesses involved in similar types of activities will face similar problems in applying BS 5750 (eg how is *4.11 Inspection Measuring and Test Equipment* applied to an employment bureau?). The particular industry's response to BS 5750 may be minimal, consistent but informal, or formalised through trade association recommendations (eg *Quality Assurance – Guidelines for Management Consultancy: The Management Consultancies Association*). In some industries there are 'sector schemes': common approaches to BS 5750 implementation developed by the consultancy arm of BSI or other similar bodies. An understanding of such industry approaches should be gained before starting a BS 5750 project and the implications for each stage of the work should be considered. However, a word of warning. Trade association guides and even BSI sector schemes are not mandatory. It may be sensible to follow the rest of the industry in how you apply the Standard, but you do not absolutely have to. Moreover, come the assessment, no company is measured against what is set out in such guides; the assessment is against the Standard and the Standard alone.

Methods of learning about what is happening in a particular industry include contact with the relevant trade associations, reading the trade press, and if all else fails, direct contact with similar businesses. Such research requires little effort or time and, as well as providing information on how BS 5750 is applied in a particular industry, can produce much other useful information (eg names of consultants with relevant experience).

What are other local companies doing about BS 5750?

As well as considering what is happening in an industry, it is worth developing local contacts. Undoubtedly, other firms nearby will either have just gone through the process or be at the same stage as you and even an informal chat on the phone could give useful tips and insights. Local chambers of trade can be an excellent method of making contacts. However, do not take everything at face value; a lot of rubbish, often from people who claim to 'know', is talked about BS 5750. A company was said to have failed because they had bought envelopes from a supplier who was not BS 5750 registered. Another was said to be in serious trouble because broom cupboards were not labelled. And so on. These examples are simply not credible at face value, although they may be a distorted report of some real problems (ie an inadequate purchasing system and a lack of quality documentation). The moral is to listen but be wary of basing your own work on unsubstantiated stories, however convincingly told.

Assistance from official bodies

In chapter 4 we suggested contacting the DTI and local TECs as a route to consultancy or courses. Even if it is decided to follow an entirely DIY approach, contact with (and literature from) such bodies is not wasted.

Initial contact with assessors

Whilst the selection of an assessor can be left until later in the project, there is no harm, at an early stage, in obtaining literature packs from assessors. If a written request for such material includes a very short description of the organisation and its activity, you may also find out whether a particular firm of assessors is interested in working in your industry. Some, including BSI, will carry out assessments of any types of business but others choose not to be involved in particular areas. Appendix 3 provides a list of assessor bodies.

THE TIMETABLE

It is essential to set an initial timetable for the project. It will probably have to be modified several times, but without some key target dates the project will drag on and on. It is vital to take enough time, but the quicker the new quality system is implemented, the sooner internal benefits will be realised. Also the external benefits (and payback) cannot accrue until assessment and registration is complete.

How long will, or should, the whole process take? This varies enormously between organisations and each project leader must make his own judgement based on an estimate of the activities involved and the resources available. The overall timetable falls into two major parts: design to implementation and implementation to successful assessment.

Design to implementation (ie up to chapter 10 of this book) is unlikely to take less than three months from scratch, but in most cases should be completed in well under a year. The determining factors include the complexity of the organisation and the availability of staff time (including the project leader) to carry out the necessary work. If consultants are involved, their availability may be a factor, but there would have to be some very strong arguments for using a consultancy whose work plan would delay the timetable.

The period from implementation is again unlikely to be less than three months, but in most cases ought to be no longer than nine. Once it is implemented, the company must be wholeheartedly committed to the operation of the quality system so the availability of staff time to *work* the system can never be a reason for delay (it might legitimately be a reason for delaying implementation). However, the process cycle time of a particular businesses is a factor effecting the post-implementation period. The assessors will expect to find evidence that at least the procedures covering most of the activities are being applied. In a business making large-scale capital plant, each project may span several months and the quality system cannot be assessed until a number of projects have been completed and therefore, in such a case, the process cycle time will be important. In other businesses, however, this will not be significant; in catering, for example, the core process cycle is only a matter of hours.

Another consideration affecting the implementation to assessment period is dealing with non-conformities. The issue here is not so much that mistakes in operating the system will be more common in the early days – this is inevitable – but that experience in handling the problems through the *quality triad* of internal audit, corrective action and management review (see chapter 2) must be acquired. This process will impose a minimum timetable depending on how the triad is set up to work.

Finally, the availability of assessor time may be a limiting factor. Most assessor bodies require between two and four months' notice to carry out an assessment (the starting point of the period usually being the date of application and payment of at least some of the fees). However, providing the process of selecting the assessor is dovetailed to other activities, ie is well-planned, it is unlikely, in practice, that the availability of the assessor will lengthen the overall timetable.

Taking into account, therefore, the periods required up to and after implementation, the whole project is very unlikely to be carried out in less than 6 months, but should be complete within 18.

We recommend that one of the first tasks of the project manager should be to prepare an initial timetable of major activities. A 'Gantt' chart, as illustrated in Figure 5.1, is an effective tool. The chart is divided into weekly columns (the example has 27), with the major project activities written down the side. Strips or lines are used to show the planned timing of each activity perhaps with the names of the staff principally involved also recorded. This in the example 'Procedure Development' is planned to span the weeks from 3 February to 13 April and be the responsibility of 'PJ' and 'Others'. Critical dates, eg the implementation day (1 June in the example) and the assessment, can be shown as vertical lines (which can also be used to show gaps such as works holidays). In preparing the initial timetable, judgements will have to be made about how long each major activity should take (read the rest of Part Two to help you). Inevitably, the first version of the timetable will need subsequent amendment and this will only be the first of several revisions. For this reason, even if the initial draft has limited circulation, we recommend including a version number (original, revision 1, revision 2 etc) and the date.

Once it is produced and agreed, the project manager should regularly review actual progress against the plan. Of course, the plan should not be changed every time an activity falls behind in timing but equally there is no point displaying a beautifully drafted but quite unrealistic chart. A balance must be struck, therefore, between using the timetable to control the project and modifying it to adjust to reality. It is essential to limit who can authorise timetable revisions; generally it is best to reserve this authority strictly for the project manager.

The Gantt chart can also be used for detailed sub-timetables. One could, for example, be sensibly prepared for each major activity represented in our Figure 4.1 of chapter 4. Such charts can be prepared as each stage is reached. When revisions are made to the main chart, corresponding adjustments will of course be needed in the sub-charts and perhaps vice versa – again, a reason for controlling the authority to revise.

BUDGETING

The final aspect of project planning to consider is making funds available when they are needed. Before a commitment to the project, some assessment of

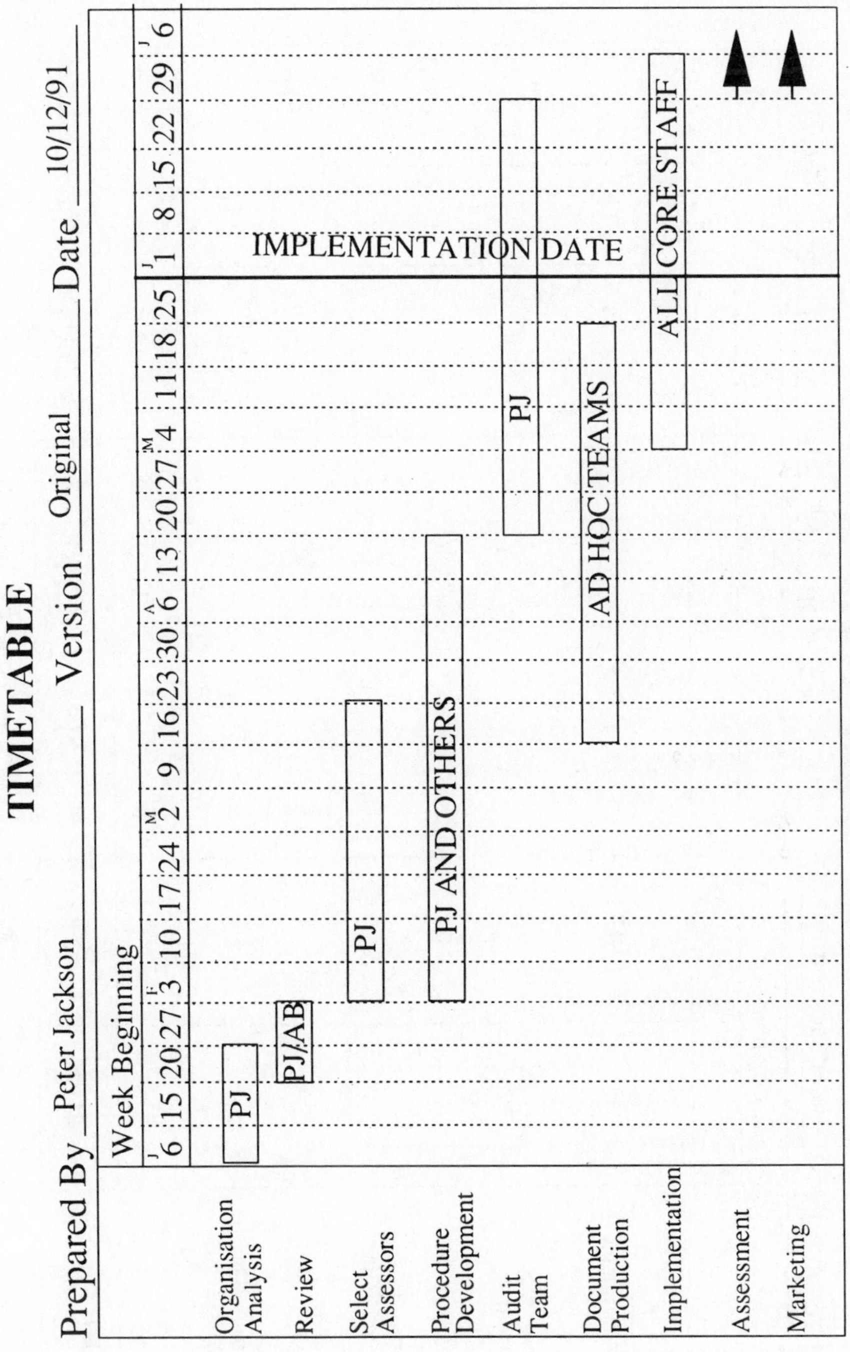

Figure 5.1 ABC Ltd BS 5750 project – timetable

BUDGET (£)

Prepared By __Peter Jackson__   Version __Original__   Date __10/12/91__

| | Week Beginning | | | | | | |
	J 6	F 3	M 2	A 6	M 4	J 1	TOTAL
Consultant				800	800	800	2,400
Training Course	400	800					1,200
Assessors				2,000			2,000
Word Processor		1,000					1,000
Other Materials				500			500
Additional Staff Costs			500	500	2,500	1,250	4,750
TOTAL	400	1,800	500	3,800	3,300	2,050	11,850

Figure 5.2 ABC Ltd BS 5750 project – budget

overall costs (see chapter 3) was probably made and this now needs translating into a cashflow plan.

The largest cost in most BS 5750 projects is usually management time, but only exceptionally do accounting systems formally cover this element. However, if the time put into the project by 'shopfloor' workers has to be made up by extra working, then a cashflow projection should take account of these types of costs. Other staff time which should be considered is the cost of any additional personnel who may be required to operate the quality system. In most smaller and medium-sized organisations this probably does not arise, although it may be hidden as additional general labour required to cover for the additional quality tasks of the existing team.

Apart from staff time, the major external costs are of consultants or training courses, if used, and the charges made by the assessment bodies. Before commitment, firm quotations of these costs should be obtained. The previous chapter gave some guidance on consultant and training costs and chapter 11 discusses the sums likely to be incurred in assessment. Other costs associated with the project might be the purchase of a word processor and (probably trivial) the expenses involved in printing and stationery. The only other major area of costs might be those that arise from any changes in the core process itself and clearly we cannot generalise in any way about these (assuming they arise at all).

The Gantt chart approach can be adapted to show the outlay of the budget over time. Figure 5.2 provides an example: consultant costs are shown to total £2,400 and arise in three equal payments in February, April and June. Again, some revision may become necessary as the project develops and the cashflow plan should be kept in step with the timetable, since when payments have to be made is often as critical as the sum involved.

6 ORGANISATION ANALYSIS

The first task in designing a quality system to meet BS 5750 is to analyse the organisation. This provides the tool for identifying the procedures that will be required and to plan how they will be related to build a coherent system.

Most organisations have a 'family tree' chart showing how departments and individuals relate in the hierarchy. This type of analysis is not irrelevant to developing a quality system, but neither is it sufficient. Nor is it what we mean by organisation analysis. Instead, the focus needs to be on the *activities* of the organisation; what happens, for example, to turn an order into a customer delivery?

This chapter shows how to carry out an appropriate analysis for almost any type of organisation. The point of the analysis – why it should be carried out at all – will become clearer in later chapters, particularly 7 and 8.

OPERATING PROCESSES AND SUPPORT ACTIVITIES

The most basic analytical division of an organisation is shown in Figure 6.1. Any organisation can be split into two parts: the operating process and support activities.

The operating process is what the organisation *does* to achieve its objectives (profits, growth, survival etc). It is its core activities and in a commercial business covers all the activities which directly turn a customer enquiry into a revenue-earning delivery. Typically this covers sales and marketing, design work, producing the product or service, delivering it and, where required, providing after-sales support.

The support activities, on the other hand, provide the environment in which the operating process can be carried on. These include purchasing, financial information, management, personnel, building and plant maintenance and similar activities. Such support activities may be centralised in the organisation, but the this need not be the case. Purchasing, for example, may be carried out by several groups each linked to a particular part of the operating process. Support activities are represented in Figure 6.1 as the base supporting the operating process.

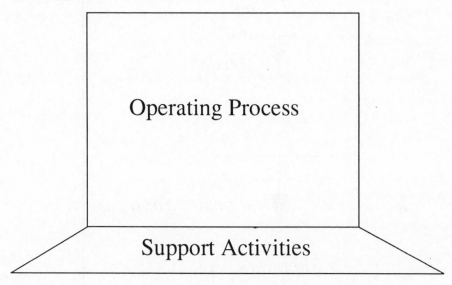

Figure 6.1 Organisational activities

For the present, we shall concentrate on the operating process and return to the support activities later.

THE OPERATING PROCESS

Most organisations will have operating processes represented by either Figure 6.2 (page 92) or Figure 6.3 (page 93). Some may have a hybrid of both basic structures (Figure 6.4, page 94).

Organisation 'A' in Figure 6.2 is typical of made-to-order or jobbing businesses. *Sales and marketing activities* generate *orders. Design* work then produces a *shopfloor specification, shopfloor activities* turn out the *product,* which may be service rather than physical goods, and *distribution* ensures it is *delivered* to a customer, who is then supported by *after-sales services.* Depending on the business, design and after-sales may not be a requirement of the process, ie they are not an element in the contract between supplier and customer. In this case the company would clearly be seeking BS 5750 Part 2 rather than Part 1. Possibly even where design and after sales are present, the decision may be taken to exclude the activity from BS 5750 – again seek Part 2 rather than Part 1.

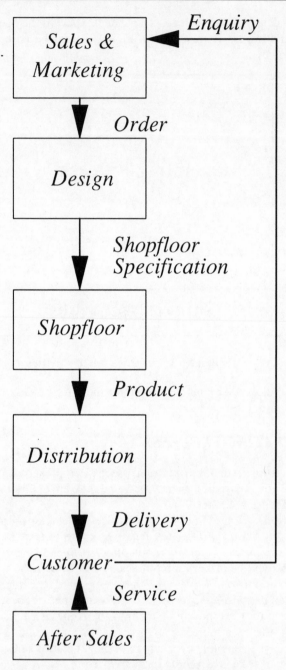

Figure 6.2 Organisation 'A' operating process

Figure 6.3 shows the operating process of another type of organisation, 'B'. The difference here is that orders are met from stock and if the requirement does not match up to the product range (or sales cannot persuade the customer that it does) the customer will go elsewhere. In this case, the shop floor feeds products into stocks held in distribution (rather than produce to specific order as in 'A') and deliveries are made from these stocks. This type of organisation usually involves a physical product. Services can rarely be held in stock; canteen catering is a rare service example of making for stock!

Organisations such as 'B' do not have design as part of the operating process, since any design work is clearly not carried out to meet the requirements of any particular customer (though, through market research, it may be planned to

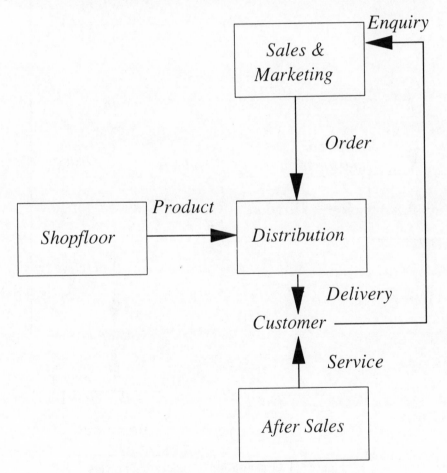

Figure 6.3 Organisation 'B' operating process

meet the needs of typical customers). Design is rather concerned with developing a standard product range and the work is probably best considered as being part of support activities. Design activities in this sort of structure may or may not be included in the scope of registration sought for BS 5750. The company may choose either Part 1 or 2 but exclusion and Part 2 is most common.

Figure 6.4 represents a hybrid organisation where some orders are met from stock while others are made to meet the specific requirement.

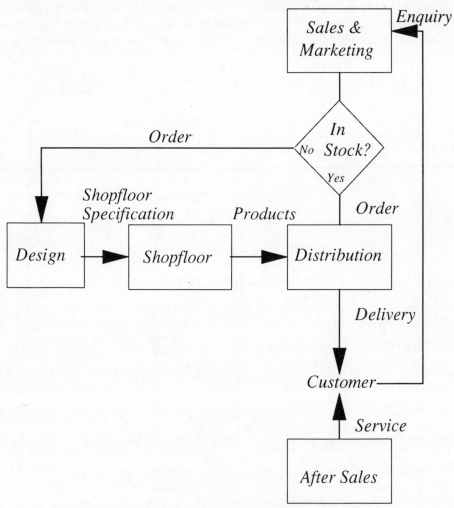

Figure 6.4 Organisation 'C' operating process

We will now look at each major part of the operating process starting with the most complex.

THE SHOPFLOOR

To avoid any confusion, we must state at the outset that although a shopfloor may be a specific area where manufacturing processes are carried out, we use the term to cover any activities involved in turning out a product or service and they need not be carried out in a factory or office area. The work, for example, may equally well be undertaken at the customers' site.

What happens within a shopfloor varies enormously between different types of businesses – for example, the activities within a solicitor's office are quite unlike those at an abattoir or chemical plant. However, all shopfloors, without exception, are built up of inter-connected chains of inputs–processes–outputs.

Figure 6.5 represents a very simple shopfloor, 'A'. It could stand for a business making wire coat-hangers. A1 shows one input, one process and one output. In the coat-hanger example, the input is wire coils, the process includes straightening and cutting the wire, forming it to shape and twisting to produce the final coat-hanger – the output. The process in the box of the figure is, however, simplified and represented as only one process. In A2 of Figure 6.5 the process is analysed in more detail to represent it as a chain of inputs–processes–outputs and where the outputs of one process become the inputs of another (shown as 'O/I'). In the coat-hanger case, the sequence might be straightening/cutting the wire P1, with the straight-cut length output fed in as an input to P2; bending to shape and finally the bent wire becoming an input to P3, the final tying. (Apologies to any manufacturer of coat-hangers reading this book; it is probably done altogether differently.)

A very important point to make is that in Figure 6.5 the representations A1 and A2 are of one and the same shopfloor. The difference is that A1 leaves the process without detail (or at a 'major process' level) while A2 provides more detail. It is possible, of course, that a third level of further of detail could be represented (perhaps not with our coat-hanger example!). Neither A1 or A2 is more or less a true model of the actual shopfloor and the level of detail needed in organisation analysis is determined solely by how the resulting analysis is used in the *review* or *procedure design* stages of developing a quality system. In practice, therefore, a judgement about the level of detail required has to be made when analysing the shopfloor. The level of detail required is that which is necessary to carry out the review and design procedures. The best practical advice we can give is to stay initially at the fairly general level and, if necessary, break down elements into more detail later.

The chain of inputs–processes–outputs has to be thought of in a very wide sense and is certainly not confined to physical inputs, processes and outputs. At

A1

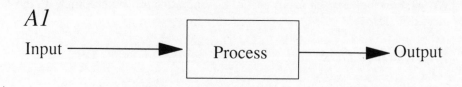

A2

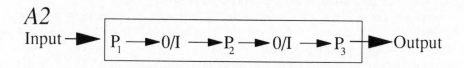

Figure 6.5 Shopfloor 'A'

an insurance brokers, for example, choosing a policy from those available on the market in order to best match the client's requirements is as much a process as machining a lock assembly. A common type of process relevant in most businesses and usually vital to quality is *testing*; obviously the forms of testing vary. In the coat-hanger example, the final process might be testing the hangers against a standard shape with any not conforming scrapped. Also a process might be passive, eg holding work stores of materials required in the process. Similarly, inputs do not have to be tangible. They can be various sorts of information, for example, the range of available policies. One sort of information, however, which we would not regard as a shopfloor input is the specification of what is to be produced since this is what connects the shopfloor to design or sales and marketing (refer back to Figure 6.2).

A special type of inputs are those supplied by a customer for incorporation in the final delivery, confusingly referred to as *purchaser supplied product* in BS 5750. This can arise in made-to-order/jobbing businesses. An example is a casting which a engineering shop machines as a final component: the customer receives back his casting with further work done to it. Examples of this sort of arrangements can also be found in services: information supplied by a client to a management consultancy can be regarded as 'incorporated' into the final product, the report of recommendations.

In shopfloor 'A' represented in Figure 6.5 we showed only one straight line of inputs–processes–outputs. Usually, the situation is more complex. Figure 6.6

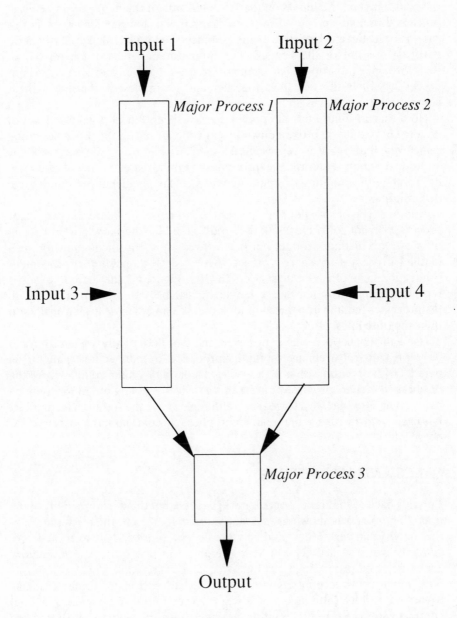

Figure 6.6 Shopfloor 'B'

represents shopfloor 'B' where two separate processes converge. Sticking with the coat-hangers, the inputs on the left-hand side of the figure could be wire, processed in major process 1 into our familiar wire hanger. However, in this case a sophisticated hanger is being produced; one which has a plastic strip covering the rail of the hanger. The input on the right of Figure 6.6 is, therefore, plastic strip which in major process 2 is cut and shaped. Major process 3 brings the two lines together and assembles the finished hanger complete with rail cover.

Note that in Figure 6.6 the processes have been left at a general level of detail. They could be broken down to show the more specific processes in the same way that A1 was represented as A2 in Figure 6.5. Also, we show additional inputs entering the processes. (In the case of the plastic strip processing, the additional input 4 could be, say, gold paint to add some decoration.)

Another type of shopfloor is represented in Figure 6.7. Here the two major processes do not converge at all; they could stand for the shopfloor processing of two quite distinct product lines. However, it is not uncommon for such parallel processes to 'share' some activities, eg a paint-shop or document production in an office-based service. In C1 of Figure 6.7 the shared process is represented by the dotted-line rectangle, but can be better shown as in C2 with the processes feeding into the common process 3 and then diverging again into their separate lines.

Using the concepts we have suggested, the shopfloor of any organisation can be represented by chains of inputs–processes–outputs, converging or in parallel with or without shared processes. Depending on the complexity of the business, the chart produced can be more or less simple – the more complex may end up looking like a large tree – although where the situation is complex, it is best to start with a general but comprehensive chart and, if necessary, add detail later.

SALES AND MARKETING

Looking back to Figures 6.2 or 6.3, it will be seen that the starting activity of the operating process is shown as *sales and marketing*. Again, the organisation of this activity can vary widely and be more or less complex. However, at a very general level, the activity can be represented in just three stages: enquiry generation and processing (encompassing advertising, direct mail, sales visits etc), preparing draft contracts and negotiating with customers, using sales skills to obtain results (although not always successfully) and agreeing a final contract with the customer (contract accepted). As indicated by the dotted line in Figure 6.8, only the later two activities (possibly even only the third) is directly relevant to BS 5750.

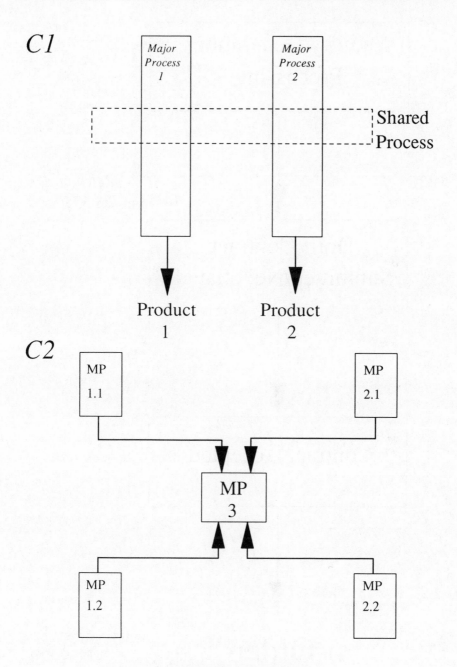

Figure 6.7 Shopfloor 'C'

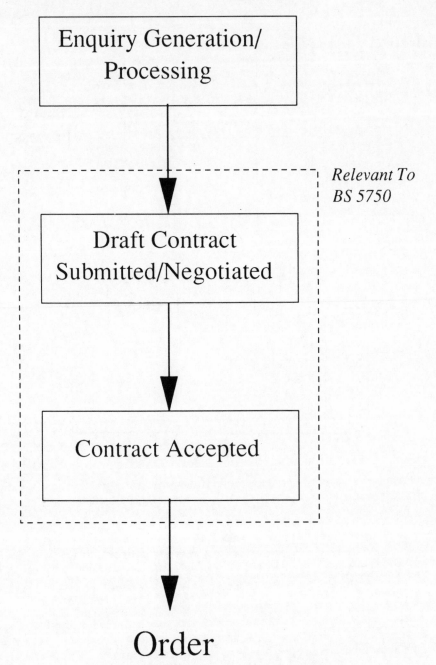

Figure 6.8 Sales and marketing activities

Generally, for the purposes of designing a quality system to meet BS 5750, the representation of sales and marketing as per Figure 6.8 is sufficient. The specific activities undertaken in each of the three boxes can, however, be usefully listed under the major headings (enquiry generation etc).

DESIGN

Design only needs to be included in the organisation analysis where it is part of the operating process and/or Part 1 of BS 5750 is being sought. Again, the possibly involved and complex activities can, at least initially, often be best represented by a three-box chart as in Figure 6.9. This is the case where design is carried out within one central department. In other organisations, however, design may be carried out within different parts of the operating process (eg in a management consultancy) and in such cases a different representation will be appropriate. The three boxes in Figure 6.9, as we show later, correspond to specific requirements of the Standard (ie Part 1). As with sales and marketing, it is probably enough to leave the analysis at this very general level with the addition of a listing of the specific activities carried out in the three boxes.

DISTRIBUTION

The activities covered by *distribution* in Figures 6.2 and 6.3 cover three principal areas:

- *Storage* In a business supplying customers from stock (as per Figure 6.3) storage is a major element in the operating process. It is clearly commercially critical – maintaining adequate stock levels to meet demand versus minimising stocking costs. Storage also has an important quality component; having maximised quality in design and on the shopfloor, the product must not be allowed to deteriorate while it is in stock. The specific action needed to ensure this will depend on the nature of the product – the requirements for the safe keeping of frozen vegetables is quite different to gravel.

  In made-to-order or jobbing businesses (as per Figure 6.2) the storage requirements are often much less onerous; the product is delivered very soon after it is made. For many services, no storage activity is involved at all.
- *Packaging* This covers all activities related to protecting finished products while in storage or transit. It normally excludes the type of packaging which is intrinsic to the production of the product: a can is used to package baked beans, but in this case it is hard to conceive of the product without its can-packaging. Staying with the example of baked beans, it is the cardboard

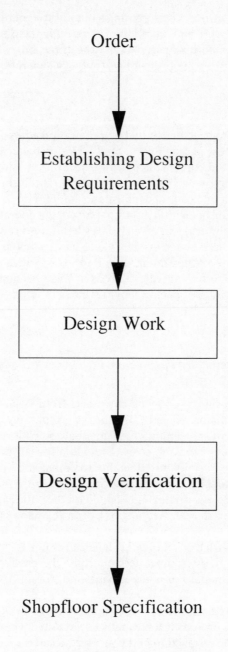

Figure 6.9 Design activities

outer carton or poly wrapping which in this case is the packaging. Packaging is as relevant to made-to-order as ex-stock businesses, although some physical products may require no packaging (eg bulk materials). Again, services seldom require packaging in the usual sense. However, a market research company registered for BS 5750 regards the physical presentation of its client reports as a packaging activity.

■ *Delivery* This aspect of distribution is as the normal usage of the word and covers the transportation of the product using either the supplier's or bought-in resources. Again, services often have no requirements in this area.

Another aspect of distribution which can either be thought of as applying to all activities or as a separate activity in its own right is handling. To ensure products are not damaged coming in or out of storage, when being packed or in delivery, they must be handled appropriately. What is appropriate depends entirely upon the nature of the product.

For the purposes of the *review* (see the next chapter 7) it is enough for the analysis of distribution to select which and how the above elements are applied, with perhaps a short description written on what is involved in each case, eg *Packaging:* Products M and N are packed in cardboard cartons in either 50s, 100s or 250s to meet different order sizes.

When it comes to developing *procedures* (chapter 8), it may be appropriate to prepare a chart of the distribution function analogous to the approach suggested for the shopfloor and built up as a sequence of inputs–processes–outputs.

AFTER-SALES

Not all organisations have after-sales activities in the sense of supporting products supplied to customers; in relation to BS 5750 it is only relevant to Part 1 registration. After-sales may, however, be applied to a service, eg following up a client's implementation of project recommendations in the case of a management consultancy. Also, some companies choose to regard positive monitoring of customers' satisfaction and compliant handling as an aspect (or the main part) of after-sales service.

Like distribution, for the purposes of the *review* it is enough to recognise that after-sales is relevant and prepare a short description of what is involved including differences across the product range and the nature and type of service given to customers. For *procedures* a more detailed analysis may be needed.

SUPPORT ACTIVITIES

Looking back to the first figure of this chapter (6.1), the operating process was shown to rest on a base of support activities. We now examine this part of an organisation in more detail.

Figure 6.10 slices support activities in two directions. The horizontal layers represent the elements of support activities which are, or are not, relevant to BS 5750. The vertical lines of the figure divide support activities into three areas of activities: resourcing, records and information and control and management.

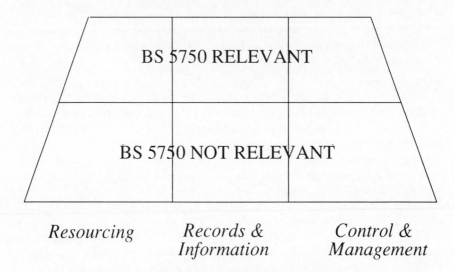

Figure 6.10 Support activities

Resourcing includes activities such as purchasing (bringing inputs into the shopfloor), providing equipment needed on the shopfloor (or elsewhere) and personnel recruitment and training. Aspects of the instances of resourcing just mentioned are relevant to BS 5750 (to be discussed in the next chapter) and can, therefore, be represented in the upper layer of the left-hand segment, while other types of resourcing, eg premises provision and maintenance, are not relevant (and fall in the lower layer of the figure).

Records and information include the activities connected with accountancy and the provision of financial information, essential in all organisations. However, although these types of records and information are vital, they are not relevant to BS 5750. The Standard, however, does have requirements in this area of support activities: those which can be described as *quality records*.

Control and management covers the general management of an organisation. In a business this will include the activities of the board of directors when deciding policy issues. This is not directly relevant to BS 5750. A type of control and management which is a requirement (in fact, several requirements) of the Standard is the control of the quality system itself (*management responsibility, internal quality audits, corrective action* and quality *document control*). Except in the rarest of cases these will not exist in an organisation prior to the setting up of a formal quality system.

For the purposes of the *review* at least, answering the questions relevant to support activities under item 6 of the Action Plan below, provides sufficient analysis.

ORGANISATION ANALYSIS ACTION PLAN

Using the concepts and approaches suggested in this chapter, we can conclude with an action plan for the reader to implement in his own organisation. However, before following this in earnest we recommend reading further chapters, at least chapters 7 and 8, since the point of the analysis work will be then so much clearer.

Organisation Analysis Action Plan

1. Produce a chart of the operating process modelled, as appropriate, on Figures 6.2, 6.3 or 6.4.

    Decide whether design and after-sales activities are carried out in the organisation. If, as well, BS 5750 Part 1 is being sought, include these in the chart.

2. Produce a chart of the shopfloor to at least a level of major processes.
   Decide whether products are supplied by customers for incorporation in the final product.

3. Confirm whether Figure 6.8 provides a reasonable representation of sales and marketing (if not, prepare an alternative to a low level of detail). Briefly describe in words the major specific activities carried out in the boxes of Figure 6.8.

4. *For BS 5750 Part 1 registration only*
   Confirm whether Figure 6.9 provides a reasonable representation of design (if not, including where design is diffuse rather than centralised, prepare a suitable alternative). Briefly describe in words the major specific activities carried out in the boxes of Figure 6.9.

5. Describe how (or if) distribution activities – storage, packaging, delivery and handling – are carried out.

5. *For BS 5750 Part 1 registration only* Briefly describe in words the after-sales operation, including any product range variations.

6. Answer the following questions about the support activities of the organisation:
   Purchasing
   How is purchasing organised, centrally or decentralised?

Is purchasing the responsibility of specialists or is it carried out by staff with a range of other duties?

Inspection, Measuring And Test Equipment

What types of such equipment (if any*) are in use in the operating process? To which specific activities are they linked?

How are they calibrated, checked for accuracy and maintained?

Some services will have no such equipment in use or could not practically apply such equipment.

Training

Is training centralised or decentralised?

In broad terms what sorts of training is carried out?

Product Identification

Can and how* are products individually identified during manufacture and afterwards?

eg a serial number permanently fixed to the product.

At the start of this chapter we distinguished the type of organisational analysis we have outlined from the 'family tree' chart. However, having carried out the work indicated by the action plan, it is worth then relating the charts and descriptions produced to the personnel and hierarchy of the organisation. Specifically, we would suggest showing on the operating structure and shopfloor charts which departments currently carry out the activities (eg use coloured lines to show the departmental responsibilities) and who are the senior staff involved. These additions will be useful when deciding who to involve at the *procedure development* and *system building* stages.

7 REVIEW

The organisation analysis described in the last chapter can now be used to decide what needs to be done to set up an effective quality system – one which meets the requirements of BS 5750. For simplicity, we refer in this chapter to the reference numbering of BS 5750 *Part 1*. Table 2.3, page 44 shows the corresponding numbering of Parts 2 and 3.

REVIEW OBJECTIVES

The primary objective of the review is to produce a list of *procedures* which will be required to meet the Standard. Procedures are documented working methods and for the purposes of this chapter include *work instructions* and *quality plans* (see chapter 9 for a description of these).

Few, if any, organisations are likely to have formally documented sets of procedures before preparing for BS 5750. However, most will have effective procedures, even if they are unwritten, covering most of their operation; it is very unlikely that the staff start the work of each day with no preconceptions of how they will work. For the important areas of the operating process there will be established methods, whether or not they are written down, and these are procedures in all but name. Possibly some of the really critical activities are written down in various forms. In some departments there may be a small manual; in others notices are pinned to the wall or memos are circulated. In carrying out the review it is important, therefore, to establish whether and in what form current procedures exist and are documented. Generally speaking, where a procedure is in place and thought to be working effectively, it is better to incorporate it into the new formal quality system than to change it. Introducing a formal quality system for the first time is a large enough task.

In preparing the list of required procedures, we are effectively deciding *how* the formal requirements of the Standard (in the case of BS 5750 Part 1, set out in twenty major headings as described in chapter 2) will be met. The second objective of the review is, therefore, to prepare a series of fairly short policy statements describing how BS 5750 is to be applied in the particular organisation. These policy statements will in due course be incorporated into (and form the bulk of) the *quality manual*; a key document in the formal quality system (see chapter 9).

The work of the review is carried out by considering in turn each element of the organisation identified in the analysis described in the previous chapter. A copy of the relevant Standard (ie either BS 5750 Part 1 or Part 2) is essential.

We divided the organisation initially into two parts, the *operating process* and *support activities*, and we will start the review in the operating process.

BS 5750 IN THE OPERATING PROCESS

Figure 7.1 is a repeat of Figure 6.2 in the previous chapter and shows the operating process of a 'make to order' or 'jobbing' type of business. In this case, however, we have included the relevant, numbered headings of BS 5750 Part 1. This shows which requirements of the Standard apply to each part of the operating process. The requirement *Contract Review – 4.3 of Part 1*, for example, applies to the sales and marketing activities, *Design Control – 4.4* applies to design etc and, as can be seen, each element in the operating process has one corresponding Standard requirement. The exception is shopfloor which unfortunately has five relevant requirements. We will deal with this most complex area first and return later to the activities which logically precede the shopfloor in the operating process.

It will be recalled that in the previous chapter we suggested that there are two fundamental forms of the operating process with Figure 6.3 (see page 93) representing the major alternative structure. The requirements of the Standard can be as easily slotted into Figure 6.3 to provide the counterpart to the representation in Figure 7.1.

BS 5750 in the shopfloor

The procedures in place on the shopfloor have to meet several requirements of the Standard. These are *4.9 Process Control, 4.10 Inspection And Testing, 4.12 Inspection and Test Status, 4.13 Control Of Non-Conforming Products* and *4.7 Purchaser Supplied Product*. These requirements were discussed in chapter 2, but should also be read in entirety in a copy of the Standard. Now is also the time to consider any recommendations set out in guides to the implantation of BS 5750 in your industry, including those from trade associations or assessment bodies such as BSI.

As we have argued elsewhere, all organisations, without exception, have shopfloors consisting of chains of inputs–processes–outputs. The first four of

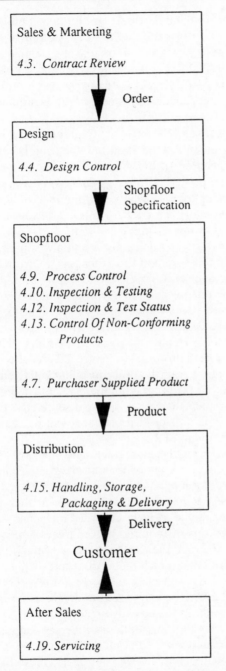

Figure 7.1 BS 5750 Part 1 in the operating process

the requirements of the Standard relevant to the shopfloor can be applied in any organisation, since they concern what happens in a process (*4.9*) or how inputs and outputs are inspected (*4.10*) and controlled once inspected (*4.12/4.13*). The remaining requirement of the shopfloor *4.7 Purchaser Supplied Product* is of a different status, since some organisations are never involved in processing product supplied by their customers. This is discussed more fully shortly.

The primary objective of the review is to prepare a list of procedures which will meet the requirements of the Standard (the contents of the procedures are decided later: see chapter 8). In the case of the shopfloor, a major issue is to resolve whether one procedure (or a *group* of procedures) will cover all the processes of the shopfloor or whether a number of procedures/groups of procedures will be more practical. Figure 7.2 reproduces the shopfloor represented in the previous chapter (see Figure 6.6) – the coat-hanger factory. If the two parallel processes 1 and 2 are essentially similar (eg both bend wire but one is used for red wire and the other for green) then it will usually be convenient to have one set of procedures covering both processes. Note that there is no fundamental objection to having a set of procedures for each of the processes, but at the very least the drafting task will be extended and once the quality system is in place, a member of staff involved in both processes will have to read two sets of virtually identical procedures. The common set of procedures to cover both processes in Figure 7.2 are labelled SF1 and this will be the provisional number of the procedure that will eventually be prepared. Staying with Figure 7.2, the process number 3 is quite different from 1 and 2 (eg it is where the complete hanger is finally assembled). For this reason it is considered that a separate set of procedures will be required and these are provisionally numbered as SF2.

In our example we have, therefore, identified that two sets of procedures will be appropriate to cover the shopfloor and meet the Standard requirements relevant to this part of the operating process (*4.9, 4.10, 4.12, 4.13*), except *4.7 Purchaser Supplied Product* which is discussed further below. The sets of required procedures can be formally recorded on a chart such as illustrated in Figure 7.3. The two sets of required procedures are recorded as provisional numbers, SF1 and SF2, and their scope described (major processes 1/2 and 3). The BS 5750 requirements which these procedures will have to meet are also recorded and when the time comes to draft the procedures, the specific requirements will have to be considered in detail. The remaining question is whether or not procedures are actually in place.

It would be surprising if the shopfloor processes – arguably the core of the business – are not carried out to some established rules or procedures, whether or not these are documented and whether or not they cover all the Standard requirements that must be addressed. It is suggested that the list of required

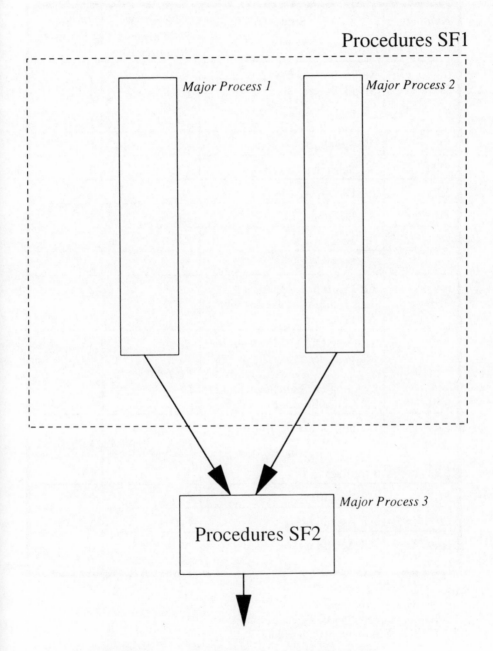

Figure 7.2 Meeting BS 5750 in the shopfloor activities

Number	Scope	BS 5750 Part 1 Requirements	Present Status *
SF1 SF2	Major Process 1 + 2 Major Process 3	} 4.9 } 4.10 } 4.12 } 4.13	} } 1 } }
SF3	All Shopfloor	4.7	0
SM1	All Sales & Marketing	4.3	1
DS1	All Design Activities	4.4	1/2
DT1	All Distribution	4.15	1
AS1	All After Sales	4.19	1
SA1	All Purchasing	4.6	1/2
SA2	All Inspection, Measuring & Test Equipment Throughout All Processes	4.11	2
SA3 SA4	Training Of Staff Involved In Major Process 1 & 2 Training Of Staff Involved In All Other Processes	} } 4.18 }	} } } 1/2 }
SA5 SA6	Output Of Major Process 1 Output Of Major Processes 2 & 3	} } 4.8 }	} } 2 } } 0
SA7	All Activities	4.16	0
SA8	All Activities	4.20	1
SA9	All Activities	4.1, 4.2, 4.5, 4.14, 4.17	0

*0 = No Existing Procedure
1 = Existing But Not Documented Procedure
2 = Existing & Documented Procedure

Figure 7.3 Specimen procedure heading list

procedures includes a notation showing whether or not current procedures exist and, if so, in what form – shown in Figure 7.3 under *Present Status*, with a notation indicating that procedures exist but not in a documented form.

With the exception of *Purchaser Supplied Product*, the primary objective of the review of the shopfloor part of the operating process is, in our example, complete and we have listed the procedures which will be required. We are now also in a position to meet the second objective of the review, which is to prepare a short policy statement showing how requirements of the Standard will be met through the company's individual quality system. In the case of *4.9 Process Control,* for example, an appropriate formal policy statement might take the form shown below:

4.9 Process Control
The company shall implement formal procedures to ensure all processes are carried out in a controlled manner with adequate documentation and monitoring to ensure control is exercised at all times.

(see procedures SF1 and SF2)

The formal policy statement, therefore, cross-references to the specific procedures which ensure the requirement is met in the quality system. As yet, the procedures are simply numbers and have yet to be written. In due course the numbering may be altered to fit the nomenclature of the quality manual. Similar formal statements can be made to cover Standard requirements *4.10, 4.12* and *4.13*.

The remaining requirement relevant to the shopfloor is *4.7 Purchaser Supplied Product*. At least in smaller businesses, the requirement to verify, adequately store and maintain purchaser-supplied product can probably be adequately covered by one set of procedures, applicable to all stages of the shopfloor and covering all processes. In Figure 7.3 the required procedures are numbered SF3 and are indicated as covering all the shopfloor processes, but as yet with no existing procedures in place. A corresponding formal policy statement can be prepared, eg:

4.7 Purchaser Supplied Product
The Company shall implement formal procedures for the verification, adequate storage and safe keeping of materials supplied by customers for incorporation into the products made for them by the Company.

(see procedures SF3)

If in the organisation analysis it has been determined that such 'purchaser supplied product' is not involved, then it would be pointless designing procedures to cover this non-existing situation and the policy statement would make this explicit, eg:

4.7 Purchaser Supplied Product
The Company does not, in its normal course of business, receive purchaser supplied product. Accordingly there are no formal procedures in place to cover this specific requirement.

BS 5750 in other parts of the operating process

Returning to Figure 7.1 we can now consider the review for all other parts of the operating process apart from the shopfloor.

The Standard requirements to be met in the sales and marketing activities of the business are *4.3 Contract Review*. In most smaller businesses it is very likely that the requirements for contract review can be adequately covered by a single set of procedures and this is the case in the example shown in Figure 7.3. In the example, the required procedures are numbered SM1, are stated to cover all of sales and marketing and are designed to meet the BS 5750 requirement *4.7*. We have assumed in the example that some procedures controlling contracts exist, but are not in a written form – they are perhaps the established methods of the sales manager. An appropriate formal policy statement can also be made, eg:

4.3 Contract Review
It shall be the Company's practice to establish a clear understanding of customers' requirements at the outset and continuously review these as the work for the customer is carried out.

All orders shall be matched to a fully documented and corresponding quotation prepared for the customer by the Company, which shall include a specification of the product to be supplied, the delivery date and the costs to be charged.

(see procedures SM1)

It is also worth noting that many of the activities within sales and marketing are not specifically addressed by BS 5750. In particular, all the marketing methods used to generate sales leads and the discussions with customers which take place *before* a contract is drafted are outside the scope of contract review, which only becomes relevant once a contract is drafted. The procedures, therefore, can narrowly address what is done once a contract is drafted and leave all other sales and marketing activities outside the scope of the formal quality system. However, a major benefit of BS 5750 lies in terms of internal efficiency and minimisation of errors (see chapter 3) and it may be considered that problems in contract drafting are best addressed at an earlier stage of the sales and marketing process, eg by ensuring that in initial meetings, salesmen obtain sufficient details of customers' requirements to enable an adequate contract to be drafted. The inclusion of activities within a quality system which are not formally addressed by the Standard, however, has a down-side which must be weighed against the benefits of taking a wider view of the scope of the quality system. Once procedures are in place and included in the quality system, they may be taken into account in the formal assessment which determines success or failure in initially gaining BS 5750. In other words, there are some dangers of making the process harder than it need be; the wider the scope of the procedures, the greater the chance that someone will fail to follow them. Procedures not only have to be drafted, they must be adhered to.

Figure 7.4 represents in detail the design activities within the operating process of a typical business seeking BS 5750 Part 1 (design activities are not relevant to Part 2). Conceptually these activities are split between establishing the requirement – which follows on logically from establishing a contract – the actual design work and, finally, design verification – checking that the design actually meets that which is required. The BS 5750 Part 1 requirements in these areas are set out in *4.4 Design Control* – a vital element of Part 1 since it is the inclusion of this which differentiates Part 1 from Part 2. Realistically, therefore, an assessment for Part 1 will include detailed consideration of a quality system's coverage and implementation in the design area. The design requirements are actually set out in *4.4* under five sub-headings and these are slotted into place in our Figure 7.4.

In most smaller manufacturing companies making to customers' orders, design work is likely to be carried out in one department and usually this is completed before manufacturing starts (as indicated in Figure 7.1). In such cases one set of procedures applicable to the single design department is likely to be most appropriate. This is the position in the example illustrated in Figure 7.3; in this case, procedures exist and are to some extent documented in notes within the design department. The procedure group is numbered as DS1 and when drafted will cover the requirements set out in *4.4 Design Control* which, it will be remembered, cover five distinct sub-headings, the contents of which must be each considered.

In some businesses, design activities may be split between a number of departments, each perhaps linked to one or more shopfloor activities. In this case, it may be appropriate to have a set of procedures for each design unit, particularly if the type of work undertaken by each is very different. However, while the particular activities may vary, the general principles of controlling the work will be the same. It may therefore be quite possible to devise a single set of design procedures which are applicable to various types of work. In general, it is better to have fewer than more separate procedures, although the purpose of procedures is to control the work and for this reason they have to be specific enough to guide staff.

In service businesses, design may be carried out diffusely at various points in the overall process with, perhaps, all key staff carrying out design functions

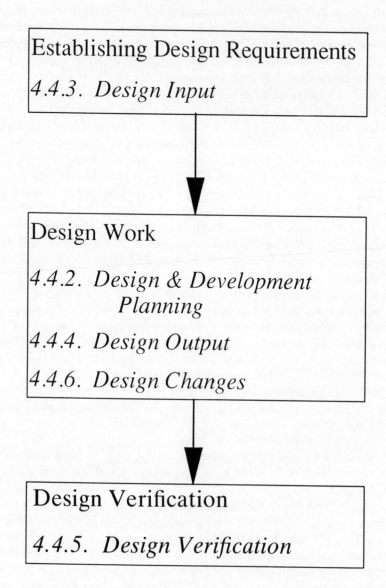

Figure 7.4 Meeting BS 5750 in design activities

alongside other activities. An individual management consultant, for example, will typically be involved in selling-in (sales and marketing), developing methods of work to meet a client's requirements (design), collecting data (shopfloor) and developing and presenting recommendations (design, shopfloor and possibly distribution). In this situation it may be more practical to include design procedures with procedures covering shopfloor activities rather than have a set of design procedures as such. Figure 7.5 shows the major sections of the procedure manual of a market research company. Although this firm is registered for BS 5750 Part 1 – and therefore includes its design activities – design is not a separate set of procedures; the activity is diffuse and covered in a number of the 'shopfloor' procedures (QS2 to QS5).

Introduction	QS 0
Commissioning	QS 1
Professional Research	QS 2
Structured Interviewing Research	QS 3
Data Processing	QS 4
Reporting	QS 5
Administration	QS 6
Quality System Control	QS 7

Note: In the example procedure groups QS 1 – QS 5 cover the operating process of the company and QS 6 and QS 7 cover the support activities.

Figure 7.5 Specimen list of procedure manual headings

For this particular company, with diffuse design activities, the relevant policy statement is as follows:

4.4 Design Control
Much of the work undertaken by the Company contains an element of design. Through specific procedures (including those referenced below) the Company will ensure adequate control of design work including in respect of –

4.4.2 Planning the design work and assigning responsibility for it to adequately trained and qualified staff and communicating these requirements amongst all parts of the Company engaged in the work.

4.4.3 Establishing the design requirements of clients.

4.4.4 Appropriately documenting the design in working papers and other documents used in projects.

4.4.5 Having checking procedures to ensure designs meet clients' requirements.

(Ref: QS 1.2.1 QS 2.3 QS 3.1 QS 3.2 QS 5.1 QS 5.2)

In the example, specific reference is made to the sub-headings of the requirement of the Standard. Given the importance attached to control of design in Part 1, this is appropriate. The policy statement of a company where design is carried out in a specific department would refer to the department (eg 'The design work of the Company is carried out by the Design Unit . . ') and give a specific procedure heading reference (eg DS1 as in Figure 7.3).

The approach to carrying out a review of the remaining parts of the operating process, Distribution and After Sales as in Figure 7.1, is much the same as for Sales and Marketing and Design. Generally, in smaller businesses, both types of activities can be best covered by one set of procedures and this is the case in the example illustrated by Figure 7.3 (DT1 – distribution, and AS1 – after-sales).

In service companies at least, some of the distribution and after-sales activities which the relevant requirements of the Standard address are not carried out. Few if any service organisations, for example, store product, packaging may be minimal and delivery carried out by normal post. Similarly, after-sales activity may not relate directly to the product or service provided. An example of an appropriate policy statement for a service company with limited involvement in distribution or after-sales is reproduced below.

> 4.15 Handling, Storage, Packaging And Delivery
> For the most part, product handling, storage and delivery practices of the Company are as normal office practice. Packaging is particularly covered* as per the reference below. Where additional service is required by the client, this shall be carried out as per the contract.
>
> *(Ref: QS 5.1.3)*

> 4.19 Servicing
> The Company's policy shall be to maintain contact with clients to determine the effectiveness of work undertaken as well as to obtain new business.
>
> *(Ref: QS 5.4.7)*

BS 5750 IN SUPPORT ACTIVITIES

Figure 7.6 conceptualises the parts of a business we classified in the previous chapter as support activities. These are grouped into three: resourcing, records and information, and control and management. The relevant requirements of BS 5750 Part 1 – over half of all the major headings of the Standard – are included in the figure.

---

*In this case the procedures are applied to the standard of printing and binding used for clients' reports rather than how they are packed for dispatch.

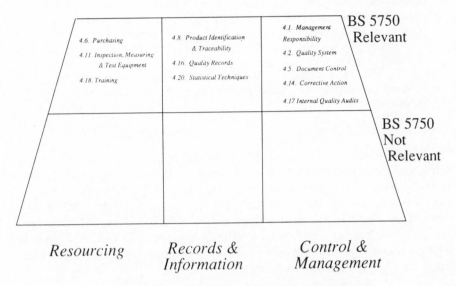

Figure 7.6 BS 5750 Part 1 in support activities

Generally speaking, the procedures required to meet these requirements are best applied company-wide. One set of procedures, for example, will normally cover all the purchasing activities of a company. This is the case in the example shown in Figure 7.3 which lists one set of procedures, SA1, covering all purchasing activities of the business. In the example, relevant purchasing procedures already exist and are at least partly documented. Exceptionally, however, even in a smaller company, purchasing may cover two or more very distinct activities (eg in a service company buying-in stationery and similar materials and, very differently, sub-contracting work to independent professional freelancers). In these circumstances it may be better to draft two distinct sets of procedures, since different staff are involved in the distinct types of purchasing.

The relevant requirement of the Standard (*4.6 Purchasing*) covers the need for assessment of suppliers (*4.6.2 Assessment Of Sub-contractors*) and ensuring that orders are adequately documented. Typically, appropriate procedures would include a system of approved suppliers with regular performance assessment (this will possibly include a provision for emergency or probationary suppliers to allow adequate flexibility in sourcing) and a requirement to place all orders in writing to approved suppliers with this documentation covering specified information. The formal policy statement would reflect the approach adopted, eg:

4.6 Purchasing
Purchases of significance to the Quality System include stationery materials and obtaining services from professional practices and similar sources. The Company shall maintain a system of Approved Supplier Lists which includes a provision for assessment of the quality of product or service provided by these suppliers (meeting 4.6.2 of BS 5750 Part 1). Orders placed with these suppliers will be in writing and in conformity with relevant procedures for documentation (meeting 4.6.3 Purchasing Data of BS 5750 Part 1).

(Ref: SA1)

The organisation analysis (as described in chapter 6) will have identified the nature and location of the inspection, measuring and test equipment used in the business. Again, in smaller businesses one set of procedures, applied throughout, is probably the best approach (as illustrated in Figure 7.3 where procedures, already existing in written form, are labelled as SA2) although when the procedures are actually drafted it may be necessary to include a separate schedule or sub-section for each type of equipment in use. A specimen policy statement could be as follows:

4.11 Inspection, Measuring And Test Equipment
It shall be the policy of the Company that a register shall be kept of all such equipment and this shall include the test status of the equipment and the method of calibration used. Where appropriate this data shall also be shown on the equipment. Wherever possible calibration shall be traceable to recognised National standards.

(Ref: SA2)

It is hard to envisage a manufacturing business without any inspection and similar equipment of this sort in use, but some types of service businesses may have none and this would be made clear in the policy statement, eg:

4.11 Inspection, Measuring And Test Equipment
The Company has no such equipment in use and consequently there are no formal procedures covering this requirement of BS 5750 Part 1.

A statement such as the above should only be made after careful thought at either the organisation analysis or review stages. If the independent assessor believes test or measuring equipment is in use, despite the company's assertion to the contrary, there will be a problem.

Businesses employing staff with a wide variation of skill levels, probably within a number of distinct departments, may find it more useful to have relevant training procedures (addressing *4.18 Training*) for each major grouping of staff. In the example in Figure 7.3, there is a separate set of procedures for staff involved in some specific activities and another set for all other staff. In the market research company covered by the list of procedures shown in Figure 7.5, all training is grouped together in 'QS 6 Administration', but as the policy statement shown below indicates, there are separate sub-sets of procedures for specific groups of staff.

> *4.18 Training*
> It shall be Company policy that all staff shall be adequately trained to carry out the tasks assigned to them and procedures are in place for specific groups of staff. The procedures include a provision for annual appraisal of training needs, plans to implement identified needs and the keeping of adequate records.
>
> *(Ref: QS 6.1–QS 6.4)*

Three requirements of the Standard can be regarded as aspects of records and information: *4.8 Product Identification And Traceability, 4.16 Quality Records and 4.20 Statistical Techniques*. In each case a single set of procedures applied company-wide is generally appropriate. The specific methods used to meet the requirements for product identification will depend on the nature of the product, but in most cases will involve unique numbering of a product or batch with this recorded on the product itself and/or in quality records. In the example in Figure 7.3 there are two quite different approaches: one for the output of a particular process and another for the products of all other activities. In this case it is considered useful to have a set of procedures specific to the 'special' process (SA5). In the example in Figure 7.3, the outputs of all processes except number 1 have no existing procedure or method for identification and new procedures will be required in these areas.

The requirements for quality records in BS 5750 Part 1 (*4.16*) concern how such data is filed and stored. The *need* for such records is specified under other headings of the Standard, eg procedures addressing the requirements for purchasing (*4.6*) will be drafted to cover the need for written orders and the data included, maintaining lists of suppliers etc. A single group of procedures (meeting *4.16*) may, therefore, specify where each type of record is to be kept, in what form and for how long. It is unlikely that a company will have any such procedures in place before setting up a formal quality system (as is the case in the example in 7.3 where the required procedures are identified as SA7). An example of a relevant policy statement in this area is shown below.

> *4.16 Quality Records*
> Records relating to both the Quality System and individually identified projects shall be maintained to provide evidence of the operation of the Quality System.

Procedures shall specify where, how and for what length of time each type of record shall be kept.

(Ref: SA7)

In chapter 2 we commented on the rather peculiar and arbitrary inclusion of statistical techniques in the Standard (*4.20*). Where a specific technique is regularly in use as part of controlling a specific operation, it can be usefully described in a specific set of procedures (the case in the example shown in Figure 7.3, identified as SA8). However, the appropriateness of such methods may not be so clear-cut in other businesses. Here it may be enough to make a general statement without any specific procedures being included in the quality system, eg:

4.20 Statistical Techniques
The Company shall use selected statistical techniques as and where appropriate in quality improvement exercises.

The final area of support activities relevant to BS 5750 is referred to in Figure 7.6 as control and management. Whether or not, prior to BS 5750, a company has defined procedures applicable to various areas of activity, it will almost certainly *not* have any relevance to this area, since they are only meaningful in the context of a formal and fully documented quality system. Another general point to make is that in these areas, policy and procedures are likely to be broadly similar across companies, regardless of their business. A procedure for corrective action, for example (meeting requirement *4.14*), can be as equally applicable to a brick works as a firm of solicitors, although the idiom and layout as well as some the finer details may vary to take account of the differences in organisation of the two businesses. In Figure 7.3 the procedures to cover all these requirements are referenced simply as SA9. They are applied across the whole company and it would be hard to imagine circumstances in smaller businesses where any other approach would be used. No further detail about procedures in this area is considered here, since specimen procedures are discussed and provided in the next chapter. We conclude with an example of policy statements relevant to meeting the Standard requirements for control and management.

4.1 Management Responsibility
       4.1.1 Quality Policy
       The Company has a formal documented quality policy.
       4.1.2 Organisation , Responsibility And Authority
       The Company has a formal management structure.
       All staff have responsibilities concerning quality and these are specified in relevant procedures and covered in staff training.
       A member of staff shall be appointed as management representative and have specific responsibilities for the implementation and maintenance of the Quality System.
       4.1.3 Management Review
       The Company shall hold formal review meetings to consider the working of the Quality System and ensure the Company Quality Policy is followed.

(Ref: SA9.1)

4.2 The Quality System
The Company has developed and implemented a quality system to meet the requirements of BS 5750 Part 1/ISO 9001.
    The system is documented at two levels. The first is a quality manual which sets out the Company's policy in relation to the requirements of the Standard and relates this policy to specific procedure references. The second level is a procedure manual which describes how quality is to be achieved in each area of the Company's activities.

(Ref: SA9.2)

4.5 Document Control
Quality System documents are controlled in such a way that all copies are kept up to date. Procedures cover the authority to draft and amend documents and the documentation of any changes made.

(Ref: SA9.3)

4.14 Corrective Action
It shall be the Company's policy to investigate all occurrences of non-conformity to the Quality System, with a view to preventing re-occurrence and making necessary changes to the Quality System to minimise the occurrence of such problems. This will be achieved through formal procedures for Corrective Action.

(Ref: SA9.4)

4.17 Internal Quality Audits
A programme of Internal Quality Audits shall be carried out covering all aspects of the Quality System. These audits shall establish whether the Quality System is being correctly implemented by the Company and its staff.
    A formal procedure shall ensure that Internal Quality Audits are carried out by trained and appropriate staff and to a planned schedule.

(Ref: SA9.5)

Figure 7.7 Specimen policy statements for control and management requirements of BS 5750 Part 1

8 DEVELOPING PROCEDURES

Day to day, a quality system runs on its procedures and developing them accounts for a large part of a BS 5750 project. However, as we shall continue to emphasise, in procedure development it is not only possible to spread the work load; it is essential. The more that staff are involved, the fewer the implementation problems.

In this chapter we explain in some detail what procedures are, appropriate formats for their documentation and how to organise effective procedure drafting. The principles are illustrated with two major examples.

WHAT IS A PROCEDURE?

Procedures show *how* an organisation's quality policy will be implemented, day to day, in specific areas and activities. A procedure manual is, therefore, a practical, how-to-do-it guide for staff. In chapter 4 we represented a quality system to meet BS 5750 as a pyramid and Figure 8.1 reproduces the concept.

The top of the pyramid is a formal quality policy which commits the organisation to implementing an effective system (see chapter 4 for an example of such a policy statement). However, no member of staff can actually *do* anything specific on the basis of the policy statement – virtuous it may be, but it is clearly not a practical guide. The next level of the documented system includes, among other things, a number of more specific policy statements describing how each requirement of the Standard is going to be applied in a particular organisation. In the previous chapter we recommended preparing such statements as part of the review work and examples were provided. In a few cases such policy statements provide adequate guidance for staff to implement the requirements of the Standard, but generally this is not the case. The policy statements demonstrate commitment and intention, but are short on practical guidance. Consider the example below of a statement which has already appeared in chapter 7.

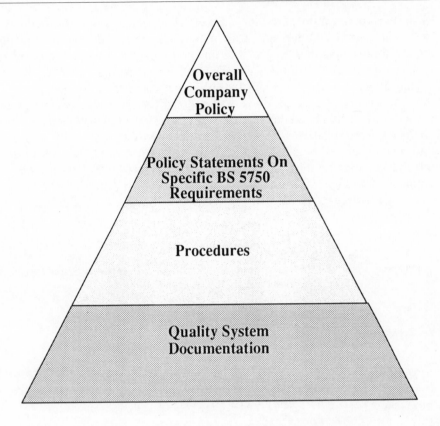

Figure 8.1 The quality document pyramid

4.1 Management Responsibility
4.1.1 Quality Policy
The Company has a formal documented quality policy.
4.1.2 Organisation, Responsibility And Authority
The Company has a formal management structure.
All staff have responsibilities concerning quality and these are specified
in relevant procedures and covered in staff training.

A member of staff shall be appointed as management representative
and have specific responsibilities for the implementation and maintenance of the Quality System.
4.1.3 Management Review
The Company shall hold formal review meetings to consider the
working of the Quality System and ensure the Company Quality Policy
is followed.

Some parts of this statement stand alone in the sense that nothing further needs to be said in order to implement the policy. The formal documented quality policy, for example, has been written and nothing further needs to be done to implement *4.1.1 Quality Policy*. The same can be said for the formal management structure. But for other important parts of the statement this is not the case. Consider the part of the statement concerning management review: more detail is needed to implement this. How often will such meetings be held? Who will attend them? What will be discussed, etc? Only with such information or instructions can the policy be implemented. An appropriate procedure describes how the commitment to management reviews will be implemented. Figure 8.2 provides an example.

PROCEDURE SA 9.1

Title   Management Review

Purpose   To define procedures to ensure that the Quality System and
                     its working is regularly reviewed.

Scope   All parts of the Quality System

References   Quality Manual
                     Procedure Manual

Definitions   *Quality Audit*: An activity carried out by persons
                     independent of the area under review, to establish whether
                     the Quality System is complied with in the area.

Documentation   Management Review Meeting Agenda – SA 9.1.3/1

Procedures
SA 9.1.1   *Frequency Of Management Review Meetings*
                     Management Review Meetings will be held at least every
                     quarter.

SA 9.1.2   *Management Review Meeting Attenders*
                     The Meetings shall be chaired by the Company Chairman
                     who may nominate another person to chair a particular
                     Meeting.
                        The Management Representative shall attend all meetings
                     and act as meeting secretary.
                        Other persons entitled to attend the Meetings shall be all
                     Directors of the Company and any other person invited to
                     attend a particular Meeting by the Chairman.

Figure 8.2 Specimen procedure

A quorum for a Meeting shall be the Chairman (or his nominee), the Management Representative and one other person entitled to attend a Meeting.

SA 9.1.3   *Agenda For Management Review Meetings*
An agenda for each meeting shall be as per Form SA 9.1.3/1.

The subjects to be covered in 'Any Other Business' shall be determined by the Chairman (or his nominee) in consultation with the Management Representative before the meeting and included in the written agenda.

The written agenda – using Form SA 9.1.3/1 – shall be circulated, by the Management Representative, one clear day before the date of the Meeting, to all persons entitled to attend the Meeting.

SA 9.1.4   *Minutes Of Management Review Meetings*
The Management Representative shall prepare minutes of each Meeting and within five days of the Meeting, circulate these minutes to all persons entitled to attend the Meeting. The minutes shall be signed by the Chairman as a true record, at the next Meeting held.

SA 9.1.3/1   **MANAGEMENT REVIEW MEETING AGENDA**
1. Date ....
   Time ....
   Place ....
2. Minutes of last Meeting
3. Points arising from 2
4. Report from the Management Representative covering:
   — Results of internal or external Quality Audits
   — Corrective Actions
   — Changes to Quality System documentation carried out since the last Meeting
5. Points arising from 4
6. Report from the Chairman of customer comments and complaints received since the last Meeting
7. Points arising from 6
8. Any other business
   a) ....
   b) ....
   c) ....
9. Action points arising from the meeting
10. Date of next meeting

Figure 8.2 Specimen procedure (*cont*)

All organisations seeking BS 5750 are required to hold management reviews and the specimen procedure can be used a model. However, the detailed contents can be varied considerably to meet the needs of a particular business. The procedure, for example, could be rather less formal (perhaps even less pompous!). A specific layout format is used for the documented procedure and again this could be quite different. We shall have more to say about procedure formats shortly.

In terms of the quality system, the point of the procedures is that they enable the requirements of BS 5750 to be implemented. Each procedure can therefore in principle be related back to the Standard. The link is through the policy statements – the management review procedure in Figure 8.2 is tied into the policy statement shown on page 125 and, therefore, to *4.1.3 Management Review* of BS 5750 Part 1. The only exception to the principle that the purpose of a procedure can be related to one or more specific requirements of the Standard is where it has been decided to include in a quality system procedures over and above the requirements of the Standard, eg financial activities.

Procedures within a quality system are always documented. However, they are not just works of literature; they must be *effective*. To be effective, we consider that procedures should meet four tests – they should be *understandable, actionable, auditable and mandatory*.

Staff involved in the area covered by a particular procedure should be able to do what is required, on the basis of what is stated in the procedure and on that basis alone. This therefore requires that a procedure is clearly expressed and understandable by staff involved in implementation. Therefore they should be written in the simplest language possible, with the author bearing in mind the comprehension abilities of the least literate member of staff involved.

It is also vital that a procedure is capable of being implemented in practice. It is unlikely that anyone preparing procedures would design, on purpose, a procedure that cannot be followed, but it is often found in the early stages of implementation that something prescribed in the procedures is not actionable in practice. For example, a procedure requiring that a certain member of staff carries out a particular check is impractical if that person is rarely on the premises. Consultation with a wide range of staff who will be involved will reduce the chance of preparing elegantly phrased, but non-actionable, procedures.

A procedure must also be auditable. A quality system is more than good intentions and it must include mechanisms to demonstrate that the system has been followed. It should be possible, therefore, to establish for each procedure *in retrospect* whether or not it has been followed and this in turn usually requires the creation of objective evidence to be built into the procedure itself. The specimen procedure in Figure 8.2, for example, is auditable by consulting the minutes of the meeting.

Clearly a procedure must be mandatory. If it is a matter of discretion whether or not staff do a particular thing, it cannot be regarded as a procedure. If a procedure is needed at all, everyone involved must be expected to follow it. Implementation is largely about ensuring that they do so, through setting in place mechanisms to monitor compliance (auditing) as well as methods to sort out problems (corrective action). In the end a quality system requires some underlying authority structure and an organisation without one (if this is possible) cannot have an effective quality system. However, while procedures are mandatory, they are not immutable. An important part of the system is to change ineffective or poor procedures in a controlled way (see chapter 9).

To conclude our general description of procedures, it is worth saying what procedures should not be. Firstly, a procedure manual is not a handbook describing how all the activities of an organisation are carried out. Some activities may be described in detail, but only as a means of stating how the quality system is to be implemented. Other activities which may be critical to the overall processes may not be mentioned at all, simply because there is no specific quality related action to undertake.

A related point is that a procedure manual is not intended to be a training manual. It is assumed that any staff engaged in the area covered by a procedure are already adequately trained to do their job (training procedures will also be covered by the quality system). The procedure manual is, therefore, not used to learn how to work the process, but to ensure that quality levels are maintained. A procedure for a machine, for example, may provide no details whatsoever about how to start up and operate it, but will detail how critical settings are to be determined (*process control*), the testing methods to be used and the records to be kept about the output (*inspection and testing*). With such procedures in place, a trained machine operative will be able to ensure the quality standards sought are attained, but an untrained person would not be able even to switch on the machine. A common problem with procedure manuals is that they are too long. Recognition that a procedure manual is not a training guide will help to keep the procedure manual to a realistic length.

PROCEDURE FORMATS

A particular format has been used in the specimen procedure in Figure 8.2 and the same format will be used in other examples elsewhere in this book. The format includes a number of features which we believe all documented procedures should include and we will discuss these shortly. However, there is nothing sacrosanct about the particular format; other styles can encompass the required features just as well and it is for each organisation to develop their own format. The important point, though, is that whatever format is adopted it should be *common to all procedures*.

Through training or in other ways, staff become familiar with the procedures which directly affect their day-to-day work. Often, however, they may require to carry out tasks in other areas of the business and consult written procedures with which they are less familiar. Auditors, including external assessors, certainly will. Comprehension is quicker and better if the format is familiar; the reader knows where to look to obtain specific types of information. A direct analogy is newspapers: there is perhaps nothing intrinsically better about the layout of the *Guardian* or the *Independent*, but the reader will find it easier to check TV programmes in whichever paper he normally reads. Moreover, with a common format it will be easier to recognise that a set of procedures are 'official' quality system documents and that they are up-to-date. The latter point is an aspect of document control, an important topic discussed later (chapter 9).

In the drafting process several authors may carry out the work. Problems will clearly occur if they are left to their own devices in terms of format. The result will be better if a model is agreed at the start of the process. Also, staff who are perhaps not used to writing substantial documents will find the task much easier if there are examples to follow.

A standard format makes the final documents look better. This may be thought trivial, but a document laid out well is more likely to be read and the procedures followed. Also, at the assessment, the first task is the desk investigation: checking that the documented system meets the requirements of the standard. The assessors are not supposed to 'award marks' for neatness, but they are human and at least will feel more positive about a quality system which is professionally presented than a scruffy collection of ill-matching pages.

The specimen procedures contain a number of features worth highlighting:

- *Numbering* A numbering system allows for accurate cross-referencing and the integration of separate procedures into a whole system, ie the procedure manual. The system used in the specimen procedures relates to the numbering first introduced in the review stage (see Figure 7.3, page 112). Many different methods of numbering are possible and none is intrinsically superior. We will refer to numbering again in the next chapter.
- *Title* The need for this is self-evident.
- *Purpose* Every procedure must have a purpose and it is a good discipline to make this explicit. It also aids implementation; staff know why the procedure is being followed. The purpose statement should be succinct and if it is found hard to draft, there is probably something wrong with the procedure – quite probably too much is being attempted in one procedure. The purpose statement is a bridge to the policy statements discussed in the previous chapter and, therefore, to the requirements of the Standard.
- *Scope* The scope of a procedure states where in the organisation it is to be applied. This might be described in terms of department (eg sales), activity

(eg purchasing), process (eg wire cutting and bending) or, in the case of system management procedures, in terms of the quality system itself (as in the earlier specimen procedure). Making the scope explicit helps practical implementation; staff know where a procedure applies.

- *References* To carry out a procedure, we may need to consult other instructions or guidelines. These may be either internal or external to the quality system. Internal references are usually to other specific procedures (which can be identified by name or number) although in the specimen procedure the reference is to the whole of the documented quality system. External references are to a document which is not created within the quality system itself. A good example is a machine suppliers' handbook which details how a machine is to be set.

- *Definitions* While all procedures should be written in plain and simple language, it is sometimes essential to use a term which might not be understood by everybody (including auditors) involved in using a procedure. Most commonly, this will be a technical term applied to some part of a process or it may be a quality system term (eg auditing). The solution to such a problem is to include formal definitions. However, this leads to the very practical problem of where to draw the line. Which terms should be defined? There is no simple answer to this, although as a general rule we suggest that a term need not be defined if it can be confidently expected that someone trained in the activity covered would recognise and understand the term. (For example, questionnaire editing may not generally be understood, but is likely to be a familiar term in a market research company.) Also, we would suggest that a set of procedures should need relatively few accompanying definitions; if there is a large number, the procedures should be re-written in plain English. Abbreviations can also be explained including those which have an in-house usage (eg GBH3) but are incomprehensible to outsiders such as an assessor.

- *Documentation* As we have already argued, a procedure must be auditable and therefore there needs to be objective evidence that the procedure has been followed. Generally, this requires documentation. This can be of various sorts (including electronic data), but in most systems documentation means forms or ledgers. It is this aspect of a quality system that sometimes has given BS 5750 a bad press – BS 5750 is nothing but a lot of useless form filling! In principle, the contrary case is irrefutable: the quality system should only be adopted if it leads to net benefits to the organisation (see chapter 3) and all procedures in a system should be necessary to the system. A procedure can only be effective if it is auditable and therefore the documentation required is beneficial. All this is true and logical, but everyone knows that in practice quality systems can accrue forms like a ship collects barnacles (and the remedy is the same in both cases – periodic scrapping).

While objective evidence is required for every procedure, it does not follow that each needs its own and separate form. One form or ledger may provide the quality data for several procedures. Also, a procedure read in isolation may not call for a record to be made, but other procedures linked logically or through workflow, do specifically have a documentation requirement.

Just as users of procedures must be able to clearly understand them, it should be transparent what documentation is required to carry out a procedure. This is best achieved through a numbering system (in the specimen procedure, the form is numbered to match the relevant part of the procedures) and by explicitly identifying the documentation adjacent to the relevant text. As in the example, the forms relating to a set of procedures can also usefully be listed at the beginning or end of the procedure.

- *Procedures* These are the crux. They contain the substance of the procedure. They are best laid out as short paragraphs, perhaps with numbering as in the specimen procedure, and with sub-titling. The reader can then quickly find what is required.
- *Responsibility* It should be clear in procedures which staff are responsible for doing particular tasks. In the specimen text the responsibility is contained at appropriate points within the procedures themselves. Another approach is to state explicitly the responsibilities under a separate sub-heading.

The example discussed is just one approach to the layout and formatting of procedures. We consider it a workman-like model, but we make no claim that it is the best possible. Others may be much better. What is important, though, is consistency – decide on a suitable layout and format and use it for all procedures.

FROM THE REVIEW TO PROCEDURES

The review (see the last chapter) will have identified (see Figure 7.3, page 112) a list of procedure headings (eg tentatively numbered SF1, SF2 etc in Figure 7.3). This list will also show the scope of the procedures (the parts of the operation they apply to), the requirements of BS 5750 to be met through the procedures and whether the procedures already exist including in an unwritten form. The procedures under each heading can now be developed and we will show how this is done through a detailed example.

In a small organisation the person responsible for the development of procedures – often the project manager – may have a good working knowledge of all the activities of the business. In these circumstances there is a temptation to go off into a corner and start writing procedures. This must be resisted. It is essential that the development of procedures involves as many staff as possible. Only through this type of involvement will staff feel the procedures to be their own rather than imposed from above. This is vital because procedures must be implemented as well as written and those which are not 'owned' will not be followed. Neither is this a case of management public relations, which much of so-called employee involvement amounts to (management decide a policy and through meetings persuade the workers that they have spontaneously developed it). Procedures developed without staff involvement will fail, not just because they are resented (which they will be), but because they will be flawed and impractical. However knowledgeable the procedure author, he will not know the processes in sufficient detail to develop valid procedures. The level of understanding required can only be gained from those involved day to day in working the process.

There are various possible ways of organising staff involvement. At the simplest, all staff from the relevant department or process area can meet together and, starting with a blank sheet of paper, decide what procedures are needed. In practice, however, they must be led effectively. The person given the leadership task by the project leader will need to focus the group, ie enable them to understand what the goal is and provide the tools necessary to produce satisfactory documented procedures. The leader may even start with his own very rough set of procedures as an opener to discussion, but this has the danger that the 'amateurs' just accept the suggestions without true involvement. Where the group involved is too big to sensibly meet together at once – or cannot all be spared together from day-to-day work – a representative sub-group can be brought together or the larger group can be split into two or more parallel groups. If a sub-group is used to represent the whole, it should be reasonably representative and certainly not just the department manager and shift foreman.

The most effective tool to use with a group is the flowchart. As we have discussed earlier (see chapter 6 on organisation analysis), all activities of any business can be represented as a sequence of inputs–processes–outputs. At the organisation analysis stage we suggested charting the whole organisation, but only at a fairly general level with the details left unrepresented within larger 'boxes' – the processes involved in cutting and bending the wire to produce the coat-hanger, for example, might just be left as one box representing all the processes involved. At the procedure writing stage, a detailed flowchart should be produced of all the activities making up the process to be covered by the procedures. Returning to the example represented by Figure 7.3, the procedures numbered SF1 require a detailed flowchart to be produced of processes 1 and 2 (see Figure 7.2, page 111). However, in this case, as we stated earlier, both processes are substantially the same and we anticipated that a singe set of procedures would adequately cover each. Therefore, one flowchart will probably adequately represent both processes. (It is probably best to produce a flowchart for process 1 and then check if it also represents process 2.)

The advantages of using a flowchart as a tool in procedure development is that any process is almost always easier to understand in chart than in word form – we can see the flow of inputs, processes and outputs. This is true even if the work is being carried out by someone accustomed to using words as a descriptive tool, but it is even more the case for a group who may never normally write anything longer than short messages or read material more demanding than the tabloid press. A graphic representation will not only be very quickly grasped, but members of the procedure development group will soon feel confident enough to create their own charts or amend a first draft. In practice, the group leader can either have a blank sheet and by questioning develop a first draft with the group's participation, or as a starter, prepare a very rough and even deliberately vague chart, and then have the group amend it once they have become familiar with the flowchart language.

Once a flowchart is prepared it will, of necessity, incorporate all existing procedures (because they are part of the process being drafted) and preparing a formal written set of procedures will be a relatively easy task, because what needs stating is already there in graphic form (even partly in word form, as the chart will include verbal descriptions). How all this is done will be illustrated very shortly through a worked example.

Because the chart is produced by the group involved in the process, it represents a common and, hopefully, agreed understanding of what actually happens in practice rather than what someone believes ought to happen – actual rather than ideal procedures. The picture will therefore be of warts and all. The process of drawing the chart will probably uncover some inefficient methods of operation and possibly lead to suggestions for improvement. However, on the whole it is generally better to base initial procedures on what actually happens rather than on what ought to happen. It is a big enough task to train staff to follow formal documented procedures without changing the working practices at the same time. Change them later, once the quality system is working, by all means. In fact the formalisation of working methods represented by written procedures provides a means of identifying the need for change – a quality system is always dynamic in this sense. However, we cannot be categorical on this issue; some inefficiencies will be so glaring that change will be irresistible at the time of procedure development. Also, the procedures must be adequate to meet the requirements of the Standard and if the existing practices omit activities which are judged to be needed to meet the Standard, some changes – usually additional procedures – will be essential. If, for example, the final product is just not inspected at all, new procedures will have to be introduced to meet the BS 5750 requirements for final inspection.

To ensure that the requirements of BS 5750 are met through the procedures, the person responsible for their development must know both which requirements are to be met and the contents of these requirements. The review will have identified for each set of procedures the requirements of the Standard which must be covered (eg in Figure 7.3, page 112 procedures SF1 must meet *4.9, 4.10, 4.12* and *4.13* of BS 5750 Part 1). Clearly the contents of these requirements must be understood by the person responsible for developing the procedures and leading the staff group involved. However, the group itself does not need to know the requirements in any detail and the best approach may be for the leader, having read and considered the requirements, to make up a very brief summary in headline form, as in Figure 8.3 below, for example.

---

* Control what is happening (*4.9 Process Control*)
* Inspect:
    What goes in
    What is done
    And what comes out
    And keep records (*4.10 Inspection And Testing*)
* How do we know if the product has passed inspection (*4.12 Inspection And Test Status*)
* What happens to it if it does not pass (*4.13 Control Of Non-conforming Product*)

Figure 8.3 BS 5750 requirement summary

At an appropriate time the group can then be asked to consider whether the activities represented in the flowchart adequately cover the requirements summarised in the headline list. Once the procedures are written the author can consider again, by reference to a copy of the full Standard, whether the necessary requirements of the Standard are being met.

The group involved in preparing the flowchart will not normally be involved in the actual writing work required to produce the finished procedures – even if they are skilled wordsmiths, a committee is a poor author. Instead, the task will probably be undertaken by the group leader or a member of the group picked as likely to be a capable author. As mentioned earlier, there should by this stage be an agreed format and layout and possibly a specimen set of procedures to use as a model. Once a first draft is prepared, the group should be reconvened, the leader should show the link between flowchart and the procedures and present the written document. The group can then be asked to comment on both the coverage achieved by the procedures and their clarity. In future, will these written procedures be actionable by the group most involved in implementation?

DEVELOPING PROCEDURES – A WORKED EXAMPLE

The example used to show how procedures are developed is based on the wire coat-hanger manufacturer introduced in earlier chapters. All the shopfloor activities of the business are represented in Figure 7.2 (see page 111). Fundamentally, the process is split into two parts: cutting and bending the wire, and final assembly. We shall focus on the procedure for cutting and bending, which in the review we numbered as SF1 (covering two parallel lines). The review identified that procedures existed for this process, but in an unwritten form. The requirements of BS 5750 Part 1 to be met through procedures for *all* shopfloor processes (ie both procedures for cutting and bending – SF1, and final assembly – SF2) were also identified in the review (*4.9, 4.10, 4.12* and *4.13*).

The first task in developing the procedures for cutting and bending is to prepare a flowchart. This is done with the active contribution of staff working in this production area. The procedure author leads the group and prepares a rough flowchart in the meeting (either from a completely blank sheet or starting with his own initial rough). The flowchart emerging in the meeting will be rich in detail through the contributions of all staff, but will also be a mess with crossings-out, changes and notes added through the group's participation.

Following the meeting the procedure author neatens and re-draws the flowchart in a legible form. Figure 8.4 shows this first neat draft. If the author has any doubts, the chart should be presented to the group for checking.

The flowchart as it stands could be the basis for one set of procedures. However, the author should consider whether it would be better to cover the whole cutting and bending process with a number of separate procedures. The chart in Figure 8.4 is fairly complex and it may be better to consider splitting it into a number of separate charts with corresponding sets of procedures developed. Possible changes of this sort to consider in the example include:

- The setting of the cutting machine and the associated inspection could be dealt with separately with its own set of procedures.
- The inspection of the initial output of the bending machine could similarly be covered separately.
- Arguably, there is a natural division of the process between cutting and bending and it might be better to cover the two stages separately.

Also, the process as described in the chart assumes that something important happens beforehand. The material used to make the hangers is checked by stores. This points to the need for a separate procedure in this area (later to be numbered SF 1.1).

Undoubtedly other changes and sub-divisions of the flowchart could be considered and there can be no hard and fast rules. The best approach is whatever leads to the clearest and most easy to implement procedures. All that

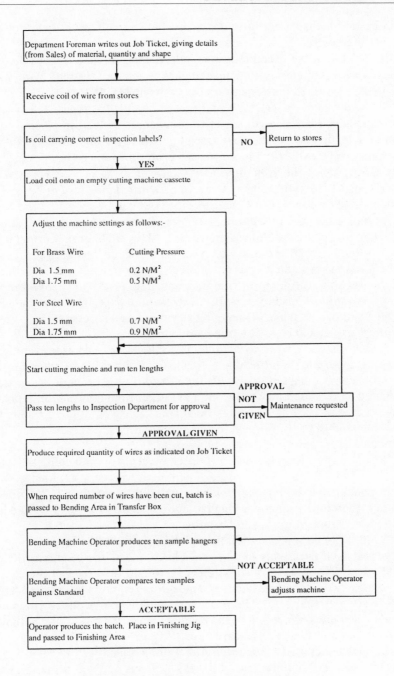

Figure 8.4 Flowchart example – initial

can be said is that procedures are generally easier to use if they are shorter rather than longer.

In the case of the example, it was judged appropriate to regard the setting and checking of the cutting machine as a separate activity with its own procedure (with the information already available, this separate procedure could be developed). The flowchart is then modified as Figure 8.5. The chart now includes references to separate procedures for coil inspection, cutting machine setting and to the next 'downline' process – assembly and finishing.

As discussed earlier in this chapter, all procedures should be auditable; after the event, we ought to be able to establish that the procedures have been followed. As it stands, the process produces little in the way of documentary evidence. Any occurrence of uninspected coils will be shown on the relevant inspection label (or by its absence), but this documentation really belongs to a separate procedure. Nothing is produced to show whether the correct number of lengths has been produced or whether the shape test carried out in the bending area has actually been completed. The most obvious remedy here is to design separate forms to provide these records. However, across the whole company, this will lead to the sort of explosion of paperwork that can give BS 5750 a bad name. While documentary evidence is a necessity, the number of forms in use should be kept to the bare minimum.

A good practice, when developing procedures, is to consider whether any existing documentation (including documentation arising from an 'upstream' activity) can be adapted to provide the record. In the example, the process is initiated by the foreman writing out a job ticket from information supplied by sales. Can this existing document be adapted to cover all the documentation requirements of the cutting and bending procedures and perhaps even the later activities in the finishing and assembly area?

Whether a new form has to be produced or an old one adapted, it is essential to check whether the proposed documentation will work in practice. Who is better qualified to do this than the eventual users of the form? The procedure author, therefore, prepares a rough draft of the new-style job ticket and invites comments from the cutting and bending areas.

Another important consideration is whether the activities covered by the flowchart, and eventually by the procedures, meets the requirements of BS 5750 identified in the review. In this case we decided that all the shopfloor processes, taken together, needed to meet four requirements of the Standard: *4.9, 4.10, 4.12* and *4.13*. The procedure author now needs to compare the charted activities, which will be the basis of the written procedure, with what is actually required in the Standard. For the purposes of the example we will focus on whether *4.10 – Inspection And Testing* is met.

This particular requirement of the BS 5750 has four sub-headings, each of which may be relevant to the activities:

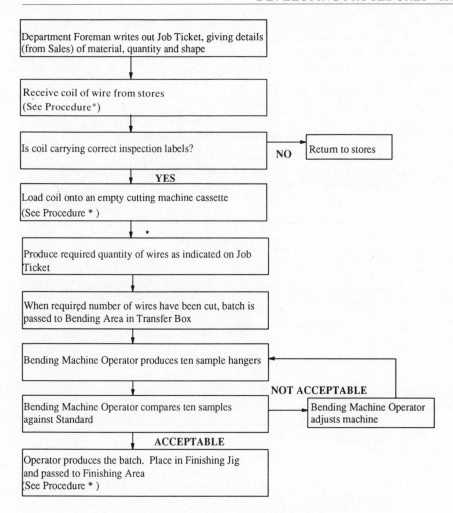

Figure 8.5 Flowchart example – modified

4.10.1 Receiving Inspection And Testing

The material passing into the process is wire coils and the flowchart indicates that the material has been inspected before reaching the process and that there is documentary evidence for this. Providing that the relevant procedure is developed for the area receiving the wire coils – stores – this requirement will be met. Whether or not this is the case, however, lies outside the activities of immediate concern.

4.10.2 In-process Inspection And Testing

In-process inspection and testing is carried out within the activities, eg at the bending stage. Also, the cutting operator certifies that the pieces are of the right size although how the test is carried out is covered by a separate procedure. If the procedures, therefore, cover this type of inspection (as they will), the requirement is met.

4.10.3 Final Inspection And Testing

The final product is not an output of the process and, therefore, this particular requirement does not arise. It will, however, be relevant to the finishing and assembly process which is referenced in the flowchart.

4.10.4 Inspection And Test Records

As discussed, thought has been given to providing documentary evidence that all the procedures have been carried out and this includes inspection and testing activities.

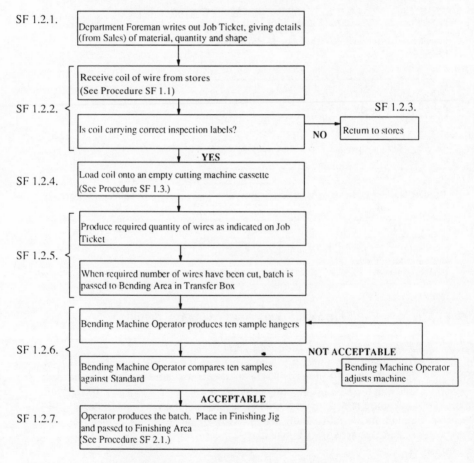

Figure 8.6 Flowchart example – numbered

In this way the procedure author is confident that, where appropriate, the requirement *4.10* of the Standard has been met. Using a similar approach, conformity to the other three requirements can also be checked. If this checking process indicates that the activities do not cover the requirements of the Standard (eg if no shape test was in use), additional activities within the process would have to be considered and incorporated into the procedures. Where this situation arises, consultation with the staff involved is particularly vital. In most cases the procedure author will not be qualified to decide how the additional activities (eg shape testing) can be practically carried out.

With these checks completed, the procedure author is now in a position to turn the flowchart into a set of written instructions. Before doing so, however, it is very useful to add an appropriate numbering notation to the chart. This will be the numbering used in the drafted procedures. Figure 8.6 illustrates this. Numbers are given to steps in the flowchart (eg SF 1.2.1) and these are then used in the drafted procedures. Other procedures are also given numbers (eg SF 1.1)

The procedures produced are shown as Figure 8.7 and follow the format used earlier. A form – the Job Ticket – has been designed to provide auditable records that the procedure has been followed (we assumed that a job ticket already existed prior to developing the procedures). References are given in the specimen document to other procedures which can be assumed to be as yet unwritten, but which can be numbered. The numbering system is a development of that used in the review (see Figure 7.3, page 112). The final reference is to an 'external' source – a machinery suppliers handbook.

PROCEDURE SF 1.2

Title	Cutting And Bending Processes
Purpose	The procedure describes the process to be used in the cutting and bending processes of the production of wire coat-hangers – from the receipt of materials, to passing the cut and bent wire to the finishing and assembly process.
Scope	The wire cutting and bending processes.
References	Material Stores: SF 1.1
	Cutting machine set-up procedures: SF 1.3
	Finishing and assembly procedures: SF 2.1
	Bending machine suppliers handbook
Definitions	None

Figure 8.7 Specimen procedure

Documentation	Job Ticket SF 1.2.1/1
Procedures	
SF 1.2.1	*Preparing The Job Ticket* The foreman of the cutting and bending process area shall prepare a Job Ticket – 1.2.1/1 – and record details of the material to be used, the quantity to be produced and the shape required.

SF 1.2.2	*Receipt Of Materials*
	The required materials shall be obtained from Stores.
	    The cutting machine operator shall determine whether the materials supplied have the correct inspection documentation attached (see SF 1.1*).
	    If this inspection documentation shows that the material has been appropriately inspected the next procedure will be as per 1.2.4.
	    If the inspection documentation is missing or is not signed as 'passed', the next procedure will be as per 1.2.3.

SF 1.2.3	*Un-inspected Material* Un-inspected material (as per SF 1.2.2) shall be returned to Stores with a note attached stating the reason for the return.
SF 1.2.4	*Loading And Setting Of The Cutting Machine* The cutting machine is then set and loaded with the material – see Machine Setting Procedure SF 1.3 (including Cutting Machine Setting Inspection – SF 1.3*). The cutting machine operator shall complete the relevant parts of the Job Ticket (SF 1.2.1/1) to record the machine loading and that the set-up is correct.

SF 1.2.5	*Cutting Of The Batch*
	The cutting machine is then run to produce the quantities shown on the Job Ticket (SF 1.2.1/1).
	    If whilst running the batch, the material runs out, all procedures from SF 1.2.2 will be followed.
	    When completed, the cut lengths making up the entire batch shall be placed in a Transfer Box.
	    The complete Transfer Box will then be passed to the bending machine area with the Job Ticket (SF 1.2.1/1) attached and the batch quantity recorded.

SF 1.2.6	*Setting Of The Bending Machine* The bending machine operator shall set the bending machine – as per the Suppliers Handbook – to produce the shape specified on the Job Ticket (SF 1.2.1/1) for the batch. The bending machine operator shall then produce a sample of ten bent hangers.

Figure 8.7 Specimen procedure (*cont*)

The bending machine operator shall compare these samples against the Standard Shape appropriate to that specified on the Job Ticket (SF 1.2.1/1).

All Standard Shapes shall be available at all times in the vicinity of the bending machine.

If the sample shapes match the appropriate Standard Shape the operator shall make entries on the Job Ticket (SF 1.2.1/1) to show the machine has been set and the setting tested and shall then proceed as per SF 1.2.7.

If the sample shapes do not match the appropriate Standard Shape the operator will repeat procedure SF 1.2.6 until a match is obtained.

SF 1.2.7   *Bending Of The Batch*
The full batch shall be run through the bending machine and the Job Ticket (SF 1.2.1/1) completed.

The bent pieces shall be placed on a Finishing Jig with the Job Ticket (SF 1.2.1/1) attached and then passed to the finishing and assembly area (see SF 2.1).

SF 1.2.1/1   **JOB TICKET**

SF 1.2.1   **Batch No** ....   **Number Required** ....
Material Finish Brass( ) Steel( )   **Diameter** .... **mm**
Shape ....
Signed ....   Date............

SF 1.2.4   **Machine Loading** ....
Signed ....   Date............

SF 1.2.5   **Number Of Cut Pieces** ......
Signed ....   Date............

SF 1.2.6   **Bending Shape Check**
Signed ....   Date............

SF 1.2.7   **Number Of Bent Pieces** ......
Signed ....   Date............

Figure 8.7 Specimen procedure (*cont*)

DEVELOPING PROCEDURES FOR THE WHOLE BUSINESS

The worked example concerned procedures for a shopfloor process within a manufacturing company. We could just as well have used a service company in the example; the basic approach would be no different. The method suggested can be used also throughout a business to produce almost all the procedure requirements identified in the review. The approach of using groups of staff closely involved in the area to be covered by the procedure is just as practical in other parts of the operating process as on the shopfloor. Sales and marketing, design, distribution and after-sales all involve groups of people who both have the essential knowledge required to produce actionable procedures and whose positive participation will be crucial to successful implementation. Also, in all these areas of the operating process, flowcharting is both practical and strongly recommended and the only situation where it may prove difficult to produce a working chart is where the process being studied appears too complex to set out on one sheet. Where this problem arises, the solution is simple: break down the whole into a number of smaller, linked processes even if the divisions are artificial (eg one production line can be split into sub-processes, even though they all happen together). In this way a full picture of the whole is built up of smaller parts, each of which can be the basis of discrete procedures. To repeat a point made earlier: shorter procedures are generally more effective at both the drafting and implementation stages.

The same principles of procedure development can also be used for some of the support activities of a business. Purchasing, for example, will involve existing staff with established if unwritten procedures and this activity can be very well described through a flowchart. However, in developing procedures for some areas of the support activities, the approach does start to falter. This is particularly the case for the procedures we described in the review as 'control and management'. The procedures required here mainly arise because a quality system is being developed. Therefore there are no existing procedures of any sort, there is no existing process to chart and no staff are as yet involved in the activity (because it is not carried out). Furthermore, the flowchart approach either does not work at all or it provides insufficient details for procedure drafting (eg try charting the activity of 'management review', the area covered by the specimen procedure in Figure 8.2). Rather than flowcharts, it is usually more appropriate in these areas to base the procedures directly on the policy statement generated in the review. Procedure writing in this case then becomes a matter of fleshing out the policy in such a way that staff can practically implement it and provide evidence that the procedure has been followed. The example given in Figure 8.2 showed how this might be done to meet the requirement for management review. In various parts of this book, specimen procedures are provided to cover all the requirements for control and management. (Apart from Figure 8.2 which provides an example of management review procedures, see also chapter 9 for document control procedures and chapter 10 for internal quality audit and corrective action procedures.) These examples provide at least a basis for drafting procedures to meet the needs of most smaller companies.

The special problems found in drafting procedures for control and management may also apply to some extent to other areas of support activities including records and information. Quality records, for example, will generally be a set of rules governing how the data is kept rather than procedures controlling a process. The same may apply to product identification. In areas such as these it is not possible to suggest 'model' procedures since the variation between different sorts of businesses is so great and a practical approach must be developed to meet individual needs.

9   BUILDING THE SYSTEM

Work carried out as part of the review (chapter 7) and procedure development (chapter 8) will produce nearly all the substantive material required for a quality system to meet BS 5750. We now show how to draw the material together and integrate it into a coherent whole.

The topics covered include a description of, and practical recommendations for, each part of the complete system. We also discuss document control and the practical implications of this concept.

THE PARTS OF THE SYSTEM

The formal documented system can be regarded as being in three distinct parts; the quality manual, the procedure manual and documentation:

- *Quality manual* The quality manual is a statement of policy. It includes the overall company quality policy (see chapter 4), together with statements on how the requirements of BS 5750 will be implemented in the particular circumstances of the company. The quality manual has a number of roles including providing important signposting to the outside assessors, whose first task in an assessment is to establish whether the documented system covers the requirements of BS 5750. A well-formated quality manual provides an effective bridge between the Standard and the actual activities (ie as per the procedures) of a company. A quality manual can also be a useful marketing tool; copies can be made available to customers seeking confirmation of the suppliers' quality assurance.

  If our recommended approach to the review is followed (see chapter 7) the substance of a quality manual will already be available, ie the statements of policy relevant to each requirement of BS 5750. All that is additionally required is to draw this together and add a suitable introduction and similar formal material. We shall shortly describe how this can be done.

- *Procedure manual* Obviously the procedure manual brings together all the procedures which have been developed to meet the requirements identified at the review stage. Apart from having a coherent numbering system (which may also have been determined at the review stage), a short introduction and a list of the procedures contained in the manual, little else is required.

  The Standard refers to documents termed *Work Instructions* and *Quality Plans*. Neither is relevant to all organisations seeking BS 5750. For convenience, we shall regard these as specialised types of procedures and discuss them later when we provide more details on building up the procedure manual.

- *Documentation* Documentation covers the blank forms required by the procedures as well as the completed forms and other records which are kept to provide evidence that the quality system has been followed. The 'master' copies of the blank forms are part of the procedures to which they relate and are therefore within the procedure manual. Clearly, however, these forms are not available for use and the system requires that copies can be made available wherever they are required. A system is also required for the safe-keeping of completed records. Where they are to be kept, for how long and who is responsible for them, are all relevant issues which need to be covered in an appropriate procedure.

Later in this chapter we will provide more detail on each the above elements of the complete system. Underlying each part of the system, however, is the concept and important practical implications of *document control* and it is this subject which we cover next.

DOCUMENT CONTROL

An encouraging piece of information is that most companies seeking BS 5750 succeed at their first assessment. However, of those who do not pass at the first attempt, the most common cause of failure is inadequate document control. This is a pity since with reasonable planning, document control should be easy to get right.

There are a number of facets of document control which we will cover in turn. However, the core of the concept is that a quality system consists of the various documents we have outlined and at any one time all staff in the organisation should be working from one and the same set of documents. This is particularly vital in the case of the procedure manual. As we have stated elsewhere, procedures must be mandatory and uniform and they clearly cannot be so if different parts of the organisation are using different versions of particular procedures. Without adequate controls to ensure uniformity, divergence is almost inevitable; particularly, once a quality system starts to change. Document control also implies authority: the documents making up the system are authorised by responsible staff following an agreed procedure.

Document control is achieved by following a number of principles and developing a procedure based on these principles:

■ *Finite and definite number of copies* Within a quality system there should be a stated number of controlled copies of both the quality manual and procedure manual and the whereabouts of each copy should be known, eg copy number 4 is kept in the sales office. Each copy should have a person responsible for its safe keeping, the copy owner, often the manager of the department where the copy is kept. To ensure that the number, location and ownership of each copy is controlled a *Circulation List* is kept and this forms part of the document control procedure. Only the copies identified on this list should be regarded as *controlled copies*. Figure 9.1 provides a specimen circulation list.

Procedure Manual Copy	Keeper	Location	Remarks
1	Management Representative	Administration	Master Copy
2	Management Representative	Administration	Auditors' copy
3	Factory Manager	Factory Office	
4	Sales Manager	Sales Office	
5	Buyer	Purchasing Office	
6	Distribution Manager	Warehouse	

Figure 9.1 Specimen circulation list

■ *Only controlled copies in use* Within the organisation only controlled copies of the quality and procedure manual (which are finite in number) should be used to implement the quality system. No other 'uncontrolled' copies should be in use within the company although uncontrolled copies of the quality manual (but not the procedure manual) may be circulated *outside* the company (see below). Controlled copies of the documents should, therefore, be distinctive and not easily copied by unauthorised staff. There are various ways of achieving this including printing the copies on special paper (eg with a red border) and having the person in charge of issuing the copies sign each page. (Bear in mind that signing will also be required as parts of the documents are revised, which can become extremely tiresome if the system includes more than a very few copies.)

■ *Accessible controlled copies* The corollary of the principle that only controlled copies of the documents should be in use is that they must be accessible to the staff required to use them; an employee can hardly be taken to task for not following a procedure if the written version is not available to him. The problem of availability could be overcome by making controlled copies available to every member of staff. However, this is most definitely not recommended; the more numerous the copies, the greater the problems in controlling them and, when the time comes, revising them.

■ *An appropriate number of copies* A decision has to be made on how many copies of the controlled documents should be printed (and listed on the circulation list) and in practice a reasonable balance has to be struck between having enough to be accessible, but not so many that control breaks down. No general guidance can be given since organisations vary so much in structure, size and physical layout – all factors which have to influence the decision. By way of illustration only, in one author's own organisation there are seven controlled copies of both the quality and the procedure manual and in practice this has been found adequate for around 75 employees spread over five distinct departments – there is a copy available in each department plus one used by the auditors and the 'master' copy kept by the person acting as management representative.

As a general rule, it may be better to start with as few copies as possible and increase the number only when it is clear that the restricted number limits practical accessibility. Also avoid the status trap: each manager above a certain level does not have to have his own personal copy. A few departmental managers may be designated manual 'owners', but even they should keep the documents where they are accessible to all their staff and not locked up in an office.

■ *All copies in use are up to date* As we shall discuss shortly, it is essential that a facility for *controlled* change of the system is built in. However, once the system starts to change, mechanisms must be in place to ensure that each controlled manual is up to date and complete. This requirement is the main reason why uncontrolled copies cannot be allowed (because they are not controlled, they are not changed at the appropriate time and become out of date). The mechanisms for ensuring copies are up to date include having one copy of the documents as the 'master copy', probably in the personal charge of the management representative, to provide a yardstick against which any other controlled copy can be judged; a system of periodic inspections of all copies to check they are up to date; and page 'plating'. Plating of each page of the manuals provides an easy means of checking whether all pages making up the procedure or section of the manual are present, the version (and, therefore, whether it is the latest version) and who has authorised the document. Figure 9.2 provides an example of such a plate. For various good reasons, we have not used plates in the specimen procedures included in the book.

SF 2.1   Page 1/5
   Reason For Issue: Revision
   Revision: 2
   Date: 1 June 1992
   Authority: John Evans

Commentary
SF 2.1 – The procedure number
Page 1/5 – The procedure consists of five pages of which this page is the first.
Reason For Issue: Revision – This version has been issued because of a change in procedures.
Revision: 2 – This is the second revision (the first and original issue might be numbered '1' or left unnumbered).
Date: 1 June 1992 – This is the date the version was issued. There needs to be a consistent policy on whether this is also the date the revised procedure was implemented – if this is not the case there should be a method of determining the implementation date.
Authority: John Evans – The change has been made on the authority of John Evans. From other sources it should be possible to establish that Mr Evans is indeed authorised to make the change – eg he is the Management Representative.

Figure 9.2 Example of page plating

■ *Controlled change*   The facility to change a quality system is essential. The first attempt to build a system will inevitably have problems and will need changing soon after implementation if the system is to work. Moreover, even an initially 'perfect' system (and none is ever perfect) will have to be revised to meet changes within the organisation and the environment in which it operates. Change to the documented system is, therefore, inevitable and desirable, but it must be carried out in a controlled way – to ensure that the changes have been thought through adequately and that they are implemented uniformally across the company.
■ *The origin of change*   If a change is to be controlled, it should originate and be agreed in a formal way. In practice, this is best achieved by allowing change only through a *Corrective Action Procedure*. Greater detail (and an example) of this type of procedure is provided in the next chapter. For the moment, it is enough to say that the procedure provides a mechanism for investigating problems found in a quality system and, where appropriate, agreeing and authorising necessary changes to solve the problem (management review). Initially, it may seem a strange concept that a quality system

is only changed when problems are identified, but our usage of the term 'problem' is in the widest sense and includes the situation where someone believes that the system would just be better for a change. Figure 9.3 illustrates the concept of all change to a quality system being made through corrective actions. The top layer of the chart represents how the problems arise and includes 'good ideas'. The corrective action box covers how the problem is investigated and a recommendation made for change (or not – not all problems, by any means, require a change to the system). Management review provides a means of deciding whether a recommendation for change should be implemented and, where this is agreed, the change mechanism makes sure that all relevant copies of the documented system are changed appropriately.

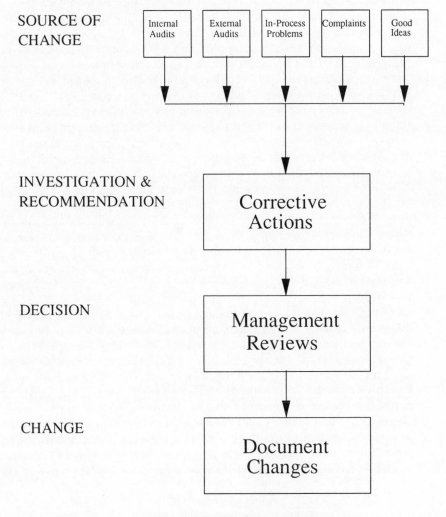

Figure 9.3 The change process

- *Responsibility for making changes* Once, through the corrective action procedure, changes are agreed and authorised, someone specific should be responsible for implementing the changes. This will usually be the management representative (see the next chapter for a discussion of this role) and, at least in smaller companies, he is likely to actually do all the practical things connected with document changes.

- *Preparing the revised documents* The first task is clearly to retype the relevant section of the document being changed. There needs to be a minimum document level at which revisions are made. This can be down to the individual page, but it is more common, in the case of the procedure manual, to change a whole procedure (which, as we argued in the previous chapter, should be fairly short) whenever a change to any part of the procedure is required. If, for example, we have decided to make a change to who shall prepare the Job Ticket in SF 1.2.1 of the specimen procedure provided in chapter 8 (see page 141), then all of SF 1.2, which is only three or four pages, will be reprinted and replaced in all controlled copies of the procedure manual. The quality manual can also be split into 'change level' sections. However, since this document is fairly short in total and generally changes are much less frequent than in the procedure manual, it may be enough to change the whole document if any part of it is changed. After retyping, the number of revised pages required to change each controlled copy of the document is printed, plus an additional copy (see below).

- *Highlighting changes* In retyping the part of the document to be changed, it is good practice to highlight in some way the part which has been revised. This can be done by underlining (providing underlining is not used for other purposes), by a vertical line beside the text or, as in the specimen procedure which follows, 'shadowing' the text. In this way, the changes are then immediately apparent to the users of the document. As time goes on, the document may be revised for a second or subsequent time. Then the latest change is highlighted and those for the previous change removed. The page 'plate' (discussed earlier) can be used to show when the change was made.

- *Document list* The procedure manual at least must include a list of all documents making up the complete manual *down to the level at which changes are made*. The list would, therefore, show procedure SF 2.1 and its title as one entry (followed by SF 2.2 etc). Against each document listed the latest revision number is shown, together with the date of the latest change. Figure 9.4 provides an example of such a list (a non-entry against a revision number in this case signifies that the document is the original issue; alternatively the number could have started at '1'). Such a document list serves a number of purposes: it is in effect the table of contents of the procedure manual; it enables a check to be made that the whole manual is complete; and it summarises all changes made to the system. A document list is also needed for the quality manual, unless it is decided to change the whole of it whenever any change is needed.

Procedure Manual			
Procedure No	Title	Revision	Date of Revision
I 1.1	Introduction	1	1 March 1992
SF 1.1	Material Store		1 January 1992
SF 1.2	Cutting & Bending		1 January 1992
SF 1.3	Cutting Machine Set-up		1 January 1992
SF 2.1	Finishing & Assembly		1 January 1992
Etc			
Etc			

Figure 9.4 Specimen document list

■ *Records of the changes* Records of all changes should be kept. This can be conveniently organised by filing in a suitable place the copies of the former pages superseded by the change (which can be those replaced in the master copy of the document), together with a copy of the new revised pages. It is desirable to annotate the superseded document with the corrective action number (see the next chapter) which led to the change and through which it was authorised. It may also prove useful to keep in the change file a log of all changes, numbered in sequential order and showing for each change the document reference, eg the procedure number and the corresponding corrective action number. Keeping records in this way is normally the responsibility of the management representative or staff working under his direct control.

■ *Making the changes* After all this we are ready actually to change the documents in all controlled copies of the procedure or quality manual. A mechanism is required to ensure that *all* controlled copies are changed within a short time. In a small company the work may be done personally by the management representative or by a member of staff reporting directly to him. However, once the number of controlled copies exceeds, say, ten or the copies are spread about geographically, such personal control becomes impractical or too expensive in time. An alternative is to circulate the new pages to the keepers of the manuals, with instructions to insert the new pages in order and *return the replaced pages to the management representative*. The latter is important both to provide evidence that the change has actually been carried out and to ensure that out-dated documents are removed from circulation. Whoever makes the changes, the replaced pages are destroyed except for the copy required for the records mentioned above. Whether the changes are carried out by the management representative or through circulation, some sort of checklist is desirable to 'tick off' each controlled copy as it is changed; a copy of the circulation list can be adapted for this purpose. Because of the importance of ensuring that all copies of the controlled documentation are changed and kept up to date, it is recommended to build into the procedures some form of routine checking of all copies. Alternatively, periodic checking can be carried out as part of internal auditing work (see the next chapter).

■ *Date of change* All staff should know when a change comes into effect and all should implement a new procedure at the same time. This is best done by making the date on the page 'plates' of the procedure correspond to the implementation date. The only problem with this is that the date has to be planned to allow for typing, printing and changing each copy of the controlled documentation.

Figure 9.5 provides a specimen procedure covering all the areas referred to in our discussion of document control. Such a procedure is required practically and is also a formal requirement of the Standard (*4.5 Document Control* – BS 5750 Part 1). However, this is only one example of an appropriate procedure (suitable for a smaller company) and may need modifying, if not radically changing, to meet the needs of an organisation.

PROCEDURE SA 9.2	
Title	Document Control
Purpose	To define procedures relevant to controlling Quality System documentation and making authorised changes to this documentation.
Scope	All contents of the Quality and Procedure Manuals and any revision of these documents.
References	Quality Manual Procedure Manual: I 1.1 SA 9.4
Definitions	*Manual Owner* A member of staff – defined by job title – responsible for the safe-keeping of Controlled Documents.
Documentation	None

Figure 9.5 Specimen procedure

Procedures

SA 9.2.1   *Responsibility*
The Management Representative is responsible for implementation of Procedures SA 9.2.

Manual Owners are responsible for the safe keeping of Controlled Documents in their charge. This includes ensuring that no changes are made to Controlled Documents except as per SA 9.2.4

SA 9.2.2   *Circulation And Document Lists*
A Circulation List and Document List is part of the Procedure Manual – see I 1.1. A Circulation List is included in the Quality Manual

A Circulation List identifies each copy of the Manual and shows the owner of the copy and where it is kept.

The Document List lists all Procedures making up the Procedure Manual and for each shows the current revision number and the date that revision was made. Whenever any changes to procedures are made (as per SA 9.2.5), the Document List shall be amended accordingly.

SA 9.2.3   *Controlled And Uncontrolled Copies Of The Quality Manual And Procedure Manual*
Controlled copies of the manuals are printed on special paper which shall be easily identifiable.

The use of uncontrolled manuals within the Company is not permitted.

Uncontrolled copies of the Quality Manual may be circulated outside the Company. These shall be identified as uncontrolled and the Company cannot give any undertaking that such uncontrolled copies are up to date.

No copy of the Procedure Manual whether controlled or uncontrolled, shall be passed outside the Company.

SA 9.2.4   *Authorised Changes To Controlled Documentation*
Changes to the Quality Manual and Procedure Manual may only be made as authorised according to the Corrective Action Procedure – see SA 9.4.

Any change to a Procedure shall require change of the whole Procedure (to the second level of numbering – eg SA 9.2.)

Any change to the Quality Manual shall require the change of the whole Quality Manual.

SA 9.2.5   *Document Change Procedure*
The Management Representative shall have a revised copy of the relevant document prepared to the usual format.

The specific changes in the document shall be identified by *shadowing the text thus*. The shadowing of text made for any previous revisions shall be removed.

Figure 9.5 Specimen procedure (*cont*)

The required number of copies of the document shall be printed on the paper used for controlled documents (the required number shall be the number of copies of the document as per its Circulation List plus one).

The Management Representative or a member of staff to whom the Management Representative shall delegate the task shall insert the new version of the document in all controlled copies of the Procedure Manual (or replace the Quality Manual with the new version) and at the same time remove the documents which the new document supersedes.

One copy of the new document and one copy of the superseded document shall be filed suitably with the relevant Corrective Action reference annotated to the superseded document to show the authority for the change.

All other copies of the superseded documents shall be destroyed.

Following any changes to the Procedure Manual, the Document List (see I 1.1) shall be amended appropriately and entries shall be made in Corrective Action records as required by the Corrective Action Procedure – see SA 9.4.

SA 9.2.6   *Inspection Of Controlled Documents*
Twice a year, the Management Representative shall inspect each controlled copy of the Quality Manual and Procedure Manual.

The inspection shall be recorded by annotating the reverse side of the front sheet of the Manual.

Any deficiency found in a Manual shall be immediately corrected and the cause of the deficiency investigated by the Corrective Action Procedure – see SA 9.4.

Figure 9.5 Specimen procedure (*cont*)

Having covered the concept of controlled documentation, we will now return to each element making up the documented system and make some practical suggestions for building them into a system.

QUALITY MANUAL

The core of the quality manual is a series of statements describing how each requirement of the Standard is to be applied in the particular company and providing cross-references to the procedure manual. Suggestions for how to draft these statements were made in chapter 7 and Figure 7.7 (page 123) gave an example of a suitable formal statement covering *4.1 – Management Responsibility* (BS 5750 Part 1), including a procedure reference (SA 9.1). If all the required statements have been prepared at the review, they can now be brought together and set out in the number sequence of the relevant Standard (ie Part 1 or 2 of BS 5750 in most cases). Brought together in this way, all the statements are likely to run to about ten A4 pages. These would be the last but largest section of the quality manual and would perhaps be preceded by a statement such as:

> The structure of this section follows the clause numbering of BS 5750 Part 1
> (or Part 2 etc)

Apart from this section, the rest of the quality manual is essentially formal. In one way or another we suggest that the contents consist of the following:

- *Title sheet* ie Quality Manual of ABC Limited. This sheet should also contain the controlled copy number (1,2, etc) unless it is an uncontrolled copy, in which case it should say so and perhaps be printed on plain rather than any special paper reserved for controlled documents (see below for the role of uncontrolled copies).
- *Contents* If it is decided to split the quality manual into a number of sections, each of which can be changed independently, the document control list can perfectly well serve as the content list. If, on the other hand, for change purposes, the manual is simply treated as a unitary document, a list with page references can be provided instead.
- *Foreword* This brief section might state that the quality manual forms part of the quality system of the ABC Company, that other parts of the system include the procedure manual. The purpose of the quality manual within the quality system can then be stated:

> This manual defines the quality policy and objectives of ABC Company and describes how the system is implemented to ensure the highest quality of service is provided to clients. Where appropriate, relevant cross references to the procedure manual are provided.

- *Circulation* A circulation list should form part of the manual. This lists all controlled copies and the keepers responsible for them (see the example given previously). It should be stated how controlled copies are to be identified (eg printed on special paper). It should also be mentioned that other uncontrolled copies of the quality manual are not to be used within the company, but that they may be made available *outside* the organisation. The point of this is that customers may go to the length of requesting copies of the quality manual as evidence of the suppliers' quality assurance, or the company may decide to use the document as a positive marketing tool and mail it to key customers. In either case, it is uncontrolled copies of the manual which go outside the company and therefore no commitment can be made that any such copy is up to date (it clearly will not be changed as part of the document control procedure).

■ *Introduction* This part of the manual is usually a very brief description of the company, including the nature of its business and its location. Half a page is probably sufficient to provide some background to a reader with no other knowledge of the organisation. A 'family tree' type diagram of the organisation can also be included in this section of the manual, although a good alternative is to attach this to the policy statement on meeting the Standard's requirement for management responsibility.

■ *Overall company quality policy* We discussed earlier the wording of an overall company quality policy and provided an example (see chapter 4). This should certainly have been drafted by the time the quality manual is put together and should be included within the document.

■ *Scope of the quality system* The quality manual should state which parts of the organisation are covered by the quality system. In most smaller companies this statement might simply be in the form:

> All activities, in all departments and at all sites of ABC Company are covered by the Quality System.

If it is intended to apply BS 5750 to only a specific part of the organisation, careful thought will have to be given to defining which parts are covered and which are not.

Suitably numbered, these various sections make up a quality manual. Each page in the controlled copies will include the 'plating' discussed earlier and be printed in the appropriate way. The whole document will usually be less than 20 pages and a fixed binding is quite suitable. Alternatively, the controlled copies of the manual can be bound loose-leaf as a separate section, but together with, the procedure manual. Copies sent outside in order to market the company should be presented as well as possible and if a significant number are involved, professional printing ought to be considered.

The quality manual is a vital part of the whole system and is usually the starting-point for the outside assessors' investigation. However, if asked what use the manual is day-to-day within the organisation, the honest answer is not a lot. It should certainly be available to staff as evidence of the organisation's commitments and the management representative and the internal audit team may need to refer to the document, but it cannot be anticipated that the rest of the staff will be using the document with any frequency. However, whether in daily use or not, every quality system must have a quality manual in some form.

THE PROCEDURE MANUAL

Unlike the quality manual, the procedure manual is in daily use and provides practical guidance for the implementation of the quality system. The contents of the manual consist of virtually nothing apart from the procedures themselves and once these are developed (as per the last chapter), all that is needed is to put them in sequence. If a numbering system was developed before or during the development of the procedures, then the sequence is already determined. Otherwise a suitable numbering system needs to be adopted, the procedures referenced and arranged in a sensible order.

Forms are an integral part of their relevant procedures and are conventionally attached at the end of each separate procedure (as in the example in chapter 8). Some additional comments on the control and circulation of forms are made later.

Apart from the procedures and the relating forms, the only other element of the procedure manual is a brief introduction. This can be limited to a statement on the purposes of the manual, a warning that only controlled copies of the procedure manual may be used within the company and an instruction that compliance with the procedures is mandatory. The circulation and document lists for the procedure manual can follow the introduction, with the latter also acting as a table of contents. Since the introduction is technically part of a controlled document, it needs to be brought within the scope of the procedure for document control. This is best done by treating it as a procedure with its own number in the system (eg I 1.1) although the layout will not match the other procedures. The circulation lists and the document lists can then be treated and numbered as forms relating to this section (eg I 1.2.1/1 Circulation List etc). It should be remembered that whenever changes are made to the procedure manual, the document list will require amendment.

Loose-leaf is the only practical binding for a procedure manual. Each procedure can then be changed separately as the need arises. It may be worth investing in a form of binding which is not commonly used within the company (eg four-hole) to discourage unauthorised tampering with the manuals. For what it costs, we would also recommend having special binders screen-printed. At a cost of only a few pounds, the finished documents will look far better and be easily identifiable as controlled documents.

We have spoken so far as though the procedure manual is one document. In a smaller company the procedures are unlikely to be so voluminous that they cannot be bound together, but in large companies the scale and diversity of the operation may entail the procedures running to several volumes. In this situation, or even where they can physically be accommodated in one binder, it may be considered appropriate to provide specific departments with only those procedures which affect their own operation. This is perfectly acceptable, although careful thought will be needed to establish just which procedures may apply; some, eg document control, apply to every part of the operation. Also, this specialised fragmentation of the manual must be specified carefully on the circulation list.

It is particularly important that only controlled copies of the procedure manual are used within the company. This can present some problems at the training stage which we will discuss in the next chapter. Like the quality manual, uncontrolled copies of the procedure manual *can* be made available outside the company, but this does not seem commercially sensible. Having gone to all the trouble and expense of developing the procedures to meet the needs of the company, it seems foolish to make copies easily available to all, including direct competitors. Generally it is more sensible to regard the document as commercially sensitive and restrict circulation to controlled copies within the company. However, it may be necessary to deviate from this policy by making specific procedures available to outsiders on a need-to-know basis (eg to sub-contractors). Also, in practice it may not be worth becoming over-zealous on the confidentiality aspect. Eventually copies of at least part of the manual are likely to go outside.

The final aspect of the procedure manual to consider is the role of *Work Instructions* and *Quality Plans* and these are covered here for convenience rather than by strict logic. Both work instructions and quality plans are specifically mentioned in the Standard (eg see *4.2 Quality System* and *4.9 Process Control* of BS 5750 Part 1). However, the reference is in a form which indicates that neither type of document is required in all situations and in all organisations. In fact, we incline to the view that the use of both is relatively exceptional – in most small companies at least.

Work instructions are best thought of as applying in organisations making standard products and where it is thought useful to supplement the procedures with a 'recipe' for each individual product. Such instructions would contain relevant details to make the specific model. In the case of our coat-hanger works, instructions could be developed for each model of hanger and detail such as the materials to be used, the cutting machine setting, the required shape, how the finished products are to be bundled and packed, etc. With a model reference and the instructions available, each part of the factory would know how to make the specific hanger required. In this case, instructions of this sort are not essential, since the information could be provided in other ways. However, they may prove to be convenient in the longer run. If they are to be used they should, of course, be controlled documents and formally linked to the procedure manual; they might all be grouped together to form a distinct procedure within the manual and, where appropriate, cross-referenced in other procedures (and therefore numbered in a way compatible with the overall numbering system). In general, our advice is not to build-in work instructions in the system initially, unless they are already in use in some form. Later, once the system has been successfully implemented, work instructions can be added, if it is agreed they offer real practical benefits.

While work instructions apply to standard products, quality plans are appropriate for large, one-off projects (although they can also be used to control a new product when it is first introduced). The most typical fields of application are building, civil engineering and large plant construction. Another feature of these plans is that their use is normally agreed by the supplier and customer and they are specifically included in the contract documentation. Also, quality plans generally involve the active intervention of the customer at various critical stages of manufacture; for example, there may be a provision for the customer to carry out quality inspections. Where they are used, specific quality plans would form part of the documentation of the quality system rather than be within the procedure manual. However, a specific procedure (or part of a wider procedure) would control when such plans should be used, their format and the responsibilities for implementation. Again, we recommend that quality plans do not form part of an initial quality system unless they are already in use within the company, in which case the need for their inclusion will be apparent. We also consider quality plans to be sufficiently specialised to make further discussion of them inappropriate in a general book.

QUALITY DOCUMENTATION

Quality documentation covers blank forms and completed ones (and other similar records). As we have stated, all blank forms should be bound in with the relevant procedures and are best numbered to link with a specific procedure (eg the form numbered SF 1.2.1/1 in the specimen procedure represented in Figure 8.6, page 140, is first referred to in procedure SF 1.2.1). Like the procedures themselves, forms will be changed to meet identified problems and to adapt to changing circumstances and it should be apparent whether a particular form is the latest available or an earlier (and outdated) version. This can be controlled by the sort of 'plating' discussed above but often this will be found impractical. One problem is that, in use, a form needs to be of full-page size, leaving no room for the plating box. An alternative is to follow the form reference number with a revision notation. Thus the first and original version of the Job Ticket in the example mentioned above would be numbered SF 1.2.1/1 and the first revision would be SF 1.2.1/1 R1, and so on.

A copy of each form is bound in the appropriate place within each controlled copy of the procedure manual, printed on any special paper which is in use and is, of course, part of the controlled documentation. Forms, however, are designed to be used and clearly those bound in the procedure manual cannot be used. In the case of the coat-hanger works, a Job Ticket form is completed for each and every batch going through the factory. The forms in use can be regarded as uncontrolled copies of the controlled documents. However, it is essential that whenever a form is changed (as per the document control procedure), the forms in use are changed to match. This can be achieved by instructing staff to make copies of forms as they require them, directly from the copy of the procedure manual accessible to them, taking care to destroy old copies whenever the form changes (the document control procedure will ensure that the copy of the form in the procedure manual is the latest version). In general, while this system meets all theoretical requirements, we consider it impractical and problematical. In making copies from the manual, there is a real danger of damaging the manual itself in some way. Also, the introduction of new forms depends on the constancy of too many staff. There is, too, a good chance that old versions of the forms will not be destroyed and become mixed up with the new ones.

At least in smaller companies it is probably better to integrate the replacement of old by new versions of a form with the procedure of document control. As part of changes to a procedure (including where, as is common, the only change is to a form associated with a particular procedure), the management representative, or someone under his direct control, can print an appropriate number of the new version of the form, take it to the point where it is kept ready for use and at the same time destroy all old versions. Variations on this type of approach can include making the print-room operator, for this purpose, an agent of the management representative. Such processes for ensuring that up-to-date versions of forms are always in use can be detailed in the relevant procedure (document control).

A final tip about blank forms is to print them all on a distinctive coloured paper reserved for that use only. It is then easy to find the quality documentation among all other papers around the premises.

The completed forms and similar records comprise *Quality Records* as per requirements *4.16* of BS 5750 Part 1. In the wording of the Standard, specific procedures are required for:

> Identification, collection, indexing, filing, storage, maintenance and disposition of quality records.

Identification can cover both the reference of the form (eg SF 1.2.1/1) and the product identification to which the particular copy of the form (or entries on it) relates. Collection, indexing, filing and storage all relate to how and where the records are to be kept together. Elsewhere, the Standard mentions the need to have the records retrievable, as obviously there is no point to them if specific records cannot be found. Maintenance covers the need to keep the records in a usable form for a defined period. How long is acceptable will vary according to the nature of the product and the practice of the business. For purposes of quality auditing, two years will generally be a sufficient time, but if the product has a long life, other factors may dictate that records are kept for a longer period. However, for the purposes of the quality system, all that is strictly necessary is to keep the records long enough to allow internal or external auditing to be carried out.

In general, there are two major approaches to such record keeping: either all the records belonging to a particular product or project can be collated together and kept centrally, or else each department or process can keep the records as they arise out of their own work. The former approach may be suitable for a service activity where records relate to discrete and sizeable jobs (eg market research commissions) and the latter may be more suitable for standard product runs. However, the appropriate choice must be made in each individual case.

Formal procedures are required for quality records specifying responsibility, where records are to be kept, how, for how long etc. Such procedures can either be integrated into the procedures which generate each record or can be specialised and cover all activities (including those we designated 'support activities', eg training and inspection, measuring and testing equipment). A 'belt and braces' approach can even be used with the procedures both integrated and drawn together as a 'summary' procedure. Whatever approach is adopted, the variation in this area between different companies and types of activity will be very wide. For this reason we cannot provide useful specimen procedures.

Since quality records are the principal means by which auditing, including that by outside assessors, is carried out, they are clearly a very important aspect of a successful quality system. No company can expect to achieve BS 5750 without keeping adequate quality records.

10 IMPLEMENTATION

A quality system is more than just documents. Well-planned quality and procedure manuals are vital, but a quality system also depends on people implementing it. The staff, including those with some specialised quality management tasks, determine whether or not the system suceeds.

In this chapter we show you how to successfully implement the quality system. Topics covered include quality system management, auditing and auditors, staff training, the start-up and what to do when the system breaks down. Two further specimen procedures, Internal Quality Audits and Corrective Action, are also included in this chapter.

QUALITY SYSTEM MANAGEMENT

The ultimate responsibility for the management of the quality system lies with the senior managers of the organisations – in smaller companies at least, the directors. However, for the system to work effectively there are a number of day-to-day tasks which must be managed. As a minimum these include:

- Responsibility for document control including issuing of forms to be used for quality system documentation (see chapter 9).
- Leading the audit team (discussed shortly).
- Administering the corrective action procedure (also discussed later in this chapter).
- Ensuring that senior management review the system and agree any necessary changes. Also, keeping minutes to provide records of the meetings.
- Implement agreed changes (see chapter 9).
- Training staff in the use of the quality system.
- Dealing with the outside assessors (see chapter 11).
- Seeing that quality records are filed appropriately.

These tasks should be the responsibility of one member of staff (although he in turn may delegate activities) and in 'BS-speak' this is the *Management Representative*. In relevant specimen procedures in this book we use this title, but it is quite acceptable to substitute another if it better fits the existing usage within a company. Often the role of management representative conveniently goes with another management job such as company secretary, financial director or office manager and providing it is anticipated that this will the case for some time, the relevant job title can be used instead of 'management representative' in the procedure manual. However, if this is the case it should be stated in the quality manual under the policy statement relating to *4.1.2 Management Responsibility – Organisation,* eg:

> The Office Manager shall act as the Management Representative and be responsible for implementing and maintaining the Quality System.

Whatever the approach, it is, of course, vital that everyone within the organisation knows who has the role of management representative.

Since he has a crucial role in the successful implementation of a quality system, the choice of the management representative is very important, although in most smaller companies there will be few candidates from whom to choose. In chapter 4 we discussed the choice of the project leader; often whoever has that role, by default, becomes the management representative. This is not necessarily a bad thing; at least initially, the project leader is probably the best qualified for the job. However, in the longer term someone else can certainly take over the role.

The qualities required for a successful management representative are really those which make any line manager successful and include the ability to plan and to lead staff. In many ways, successful implementation of a quality system depends on getting the details right and the management representative needs to be concerned about the operation of the system at a detailed level: that each procedure is followed, that the right forms are used for recording quality data, that records are filed in the correct place, etc. The management representative also needs enough authority to ensure that all staff fully participate in the quality system. 'All staff' includes a company's senior managers who, in their functional activities, will themselves now have to follow procedures as well as exhort their staff to do so. The management representative must, therefore, have the confidence to hold his ground with senior managers, as well as other staff, and he should be not much lower in standing than the main decision-makers within a company. The management representative role is, emphatically, not just a clerical job.

In many smaller companies a director will have to take on the role of management representative and juggle his time between this and his main, line management responsibilities. He must make enough time available to carry out the role effectively, although like most successful management, delegation of tasks will be a major factor in success. As discussed earlier, for example, although one of the jobs of the management representative is the updating of the controlled documentation, he does not personally have to change all the pages in the procedure manuals.

While he is important to successful implementation, the management representative cannot be the only senior member of staff involved; a quality system must not be a private domain. Other senior managers have to be involved both in their daily work and, together, through *management review meetings*. In chapter 8 a specimen procedure for management review meetings was provided and this can be adapted to meet the circumstances and style of most companies. Formal meetings of this sort need to be held at least several times a year (quarterly in the specimen procedure) and in the early stages of implementing the quality system, the meetings should be even more frequent, probably monthly. In most smaller companies the main members of the meetings are usually the directors of the company (with one acting as chairman) plus the management representative (if he is not also a director). If regular formal board meetings are held, it may be convenient to tack-on management review meetings.

A formal agenda should be part of the procedure for management review meetings and subjects for discussion will include the results of audits, corrective actions taken including the resulting decisions (to be discussed shortly), changes made to the system documentation and any customer comments (or complaints) received. Most of the information provided to the meeting will come from the management representative and it may be convenient to have this submitted in advance as a short written report, leaving plenty of time in the meeting for discussion. Minutes also form part of the formal procedure for a management review meeting and the management representative will probably be the best person to act as meeting secretary. At the assessment, evidence will be sought that management review of the quality system is carried out and the minutes of meetings will provide appropriate records.

AUDITING AND AUDITORS

Even if internal auditing were not a formal requirement of BS 5750 (it is – see *4.17 – Internal Quality Records*, BS 5750 Part 1), this very important activity would still have to be undertaken. There is simply no possibility that a quality system will work unless its implementation is checked and monitored. Only through actively seeking out deficiencies can problems be identified and solutions found.

At its simplest, auditing is establishing whether or not the requirements of the formal quality system *in every particular* are being followed. For example, in the specimen procedure for the coat-hanger works (see chapter 8, page 141), the cutting machine operator is required to make certain records on the batch job ticket. In auditing this part of the quality system, we would seek to establish that these records had been prepared in the right form; we might check this from a sample number of job tickets or, more rigorously, by tracing a sample batch of hangers through the production process and establishing whether the appropriate records have been provided.

Auditing focuses on objective evidence of compliance with the quality system. A procedure has either been followed or it has not. (If it is impossible to determine this there is something wrong with the procedure.) No judgement is made in auditing on *why* a procedure has not been followed. Possibly the required information on the job ticket was not entered because the machine operator simply forgot, or was too busy with other things. Or perhaps the procedure just could not be followed, even with the best will in the world. Any of these, or other, reasons may explain why the procedure was not followed, but we repeat that at the *auditing stage* no judgement is made about the cause for the deficiency, still less is any blame apportioned. The auditing task is, therefore, simply to identify non-compliance, not provide solutions; these come later.

Auditing requires auditors. In a smaller company auditing is usually carried out by staff with other mainstream jobs. Once the system is established, audit work may take up about one or two days per month of each auditor's time and therefore, in this sense, is not an over-heavy burden. It is advisable to have at least two auditors available at any one time; they may work efficiently as a pair, and auditing can still go ahead if one is not available. The management representative leads the audit team and in this sense is part of it, but does not have to take part in actual audits (and it is probably better if he does not).

The choice of part-time auditors is important. Again in smaller companies, there are often few candidates, but whoever is selected for the work will need at least three characteristics:

- *Independence* This has two aspects. Firstly, auditing of any area of the business must be carried out by someone who is not involved in the activities day-to-day. This is largely a practical matter; someone involved in an activity is more likely to focus on what *ought* to happen than on what *actually* happens (for much the same reason, an author does not proof-read his own work well). Auditors, therefore, are better selected from among staff not involved in the core activities of the business and may be better drawn from the administrative (eg financial) staff.

  The second aspect of independence lies in being capable of arriving at judgements and sticking with them despite pressure from other, possibly more senior, staff. Although auditing ought to be factual – the procedure has or has not been followed – and non-judgemental, a line manager may well feel threatened by any deficiencies discovered in the operation of the quality system in his domain, particularly if it appears that the problem is that staff are not putting enough effort into following the system. In such circumstances, a manager may seek to solve the problem through brow-beating the auditor and convincing him that the procedures have been followed or followed 'as well as they can'. The auditor must resist this and, despite any hostility, report that the requirements of the system are not being followed in this instance. Such independence is a personal quality, although the auditor must also feel confident that in carrying out the job, he is following the policy (and has the support) of the senior mangers of the whole company.

- *Tact* Tact is clearly linked to the second sort of independence. In order to minimise the possible stresses inherent in being audited, the auditors must deal tactfully with the staff of a department. Whatever may be sometimes thought, auditors are not there to discover and punish 'wicked' staff. If a deficiency is found, both auditor and auditee should agree that this objective fact exists, eg some job tickets do not record the machine setting. The auditor must not imply that because of this deficiency he considers the departmental staff or manager are not doing their job properly. Also, the auditor has to take up time of the staff whose work is the subject of the audit. Tact will be required to persuade staff to give the necessary time to the audit (although often this is minimal since much of the work is looking at records which should be in an accessible form). Sometimes the auditor will need to deal with staff who use shortage of time as an excuse for avoiding an audit altogether. If (after training) the auditor has not got the interpersonal skills to deal with this or similar situations, he is not suitable for the work.

- *Attention to detail* An auditor does not need technical expertise in the area subject to audit. At least in principle, auditing in the coat-hanger works requires no knowledge of wire bending. The auditor must, however, get down to detail. It is not enough that the machine operator appears to write something down now and again; the records of the machine setting etc must be in the prescribed form on the right document. The audit must be capable of identifying in detail both what is required and what has actually been done. In this case, nit-picking is a very much a virtue.

Once selected, internal auditors must be trained (there is a British Standard relevent to audit work, BS 7229). Various commercial organisations run courses aimed specifically at internal auditing. No doubt these offer valuable training, but for the smaller company it is perfectly possible for training to be organised internally by the BS 5750 project leader or, if different, the management representative. At the least, he can act as the leader of a seminar where both he and the auditors discuss their auditing responsibilities and how they will actually carry out the work in practice. The first few audits, although 'for real', can be regarded as part of the auditor training process.

Auditor training needs to be started well before the start-up day for implementing the quality system. This is because auditing should be started soon after the new system is put into action. Only through audit work can any judgement be made on whether the system is working reasonably well.

Auditing as a process should have its own procedure – a component of the system control part of the quality system. A specimen procedure for auditing is provided below, but first we discuss some of the underlying principles.

Audit records

As in other parts of the quality system, it is not enough that a procedure applies, there must be some objective evidence that it has been followed. In the specimen procedure, the records include a schedule of audits, a register and individual reports on each audit carried out. Perfectly adequate records could be kept in other ways, although the information included should be much the same.

Frequency of audit

The required frequency of internal audits depend on the size and complexity of an operation. As a minimum, every part of the quality system should be audited at least once in a year and the frequency of audit should be whatever is necessary to achieve this. Probably for the 'average' smaller company, the minimum frequency is to carry out an audit in every quarter of the year. Bearing in mind that the frequency of audit actually achieved should itself be audited (since it is a formal part of the quality system) and may be checked by the outside assessors, it is advisable to set the requirement in the formal audit procedure at a minimal level ('. . . audits shall be carried out at least once in every quarter'). In practice, it is better to do more than the minimum, and monthly audits are often useful and good practice. As already mentioned, audits should begin as soon after start-up as practical and it is advisable to hold more, rather than less, audits in the period between start-up and assessment. In this way problems can be identified and steps taken to remedy them at the earliest opportunity.

Scope of each audit

Before an audit starts, its scope must be defined. An audit taking, say, one day, including writing up the records, cannot possibly cover more than a part of the quality system. Which part it is planned to cover should be decided at the outset of each audit assignment. Broadly this coverage can be defined either in terms of the quality system itself, ie a specific number of procedures, or in organisational terms, eg the cutting and bending department and all quality procedures applying there. Deciding the scope of a particular audit is the responsibility of the management representative. Some form of audit register should be kept to record the scope of each audit (which can be numbered sequentially) along with other pertinent details.

Planning a schedule

For each year, a schedule should be prepared showing the planned audits for the year and the scope of each audit. Taken overall, the schedule will demonstrate that the whole of the quality system will be audited at least once in the year. The schedule can be in various forms but might be as simple as a one sheet year-planner or Gantt chart with the dates and coverage of each audit shown appropriately (on the schedule the date might be approximate – the month rather than a specific day). The schedule is usually drawn up by the management representative and 'published' so that concerned staff, including the auditors, know when audits are to be carried out in the year. While on an ongoing basis such schedules should be prepared at the beginning of the year, it may be better to delay preparing the first schedule for a month or two after the start-up date. The reason for this is that through lack of experience, the management representative may find it difficult to anticipate what can be achieved in one audit and thus how many will be necessary over the year to cover the whole system.

A final consideration about the audit schedule is that although it demonstrates that the activity is planned, it should never be immutable. Sometimes problems arise which suggest that a particular area should be audited as a matter of urgency even though, according to the schedule, this is not due.

Pre-audit planning

The activities of each audit should be planned beforehand. The scope of the audit should be discussed at a meeting of the management representative and auditors. Any reports of previous audits of a similar scope should be read to see what was found before and if there was a problem in a particular area, it may be appropriate to pay special attention to it and see whether the problem has recurred. The pre-audit meeting is also an opportunity for the whole team (management representative as well as auditors) to review general progress in auditing and discuss any problems. The need for additional auditor training may also need to be considered. If auditing is being carried out on a monthly basis, such general matters may not be thought worth covering at every meeting – once a quarter should be enough. Such 'special' meetings may include a training element and at least a brief record should be prepared showing what has been covered. This can then be offered as evidence that the requirements of the Standard for trained auditing staff are being met.

As well as the pre-audit meeting, other preparation includes preparing a checklist and arranging dates and times with the auditees. A checklist is purely for the benefit of the auditors and is prepared by them. It can take several forms, but a common approach is to note each specific part of the system to be covered (eg in the example provided in chapter 8, a suitable notation might be SF 1.2.5 – Cutting) together with the records which will be examined in relation to this part of the system (eg the job ticket). While an important part of the audit is to look at the evidence of objective records, it may be considered appropriate also to ask relevant staff to describe what they are supposed to do in relation to the quality system. The outside assessors may do this, so if for no other reason, it is worth rehearsing staff. The checklist can, therefore, include questions to be asked as part of the audit.

The final part of pre-audit planning is making arrangements with the staff concerned. This is not just a matter of courtesy; there is no point turning up in a department to carry out an audit if all the staff have gone off on other business. The formality of such arrangements will vary depending on the size, geography and style of the organisation. In a smaller company it may be quite enough to make a phone call the evening before the audit, while in other cases two weeks' notice may be scarcely enough. A word of warning, though: do not allow excuses about the pressure of work to delay auditing work indefinitely. The successful implementation and eventual certification to BS 5750 depends on auditing.

The audit work

It is difficult to be more expansive about what actually happens in an audit. The crux of the matter both in principle and in practice is that the auditor establishes what ought to happen as per the quality system – in nearly all cases, what is prescribed in the procedure manual – and then seeks to find what happens in practice. The latter may involve observation (eg watching the cutting machine operator to see if the procedures are followed), asking questions (eg asking the operator what he does) and, most important of all, looking for documentary evidence that the system is being followed (eg examining job tickets). In the case of documentary evidence it is clearly impractical to look at all records relevant to the procedure (eg every job ticket) and a sample must be drawn. There are various practical ways of doing this and in most cases a suitable approach should be apparent. However, the aim should be an approximation to a *random* sample, ie a sample where each item in the 'universe' being sampled has an equal chance of selection. What must be avoided is a biassed sample, eg one that excludes all those jobs that went wrong or for that matter one that only includes bad jobs. One type of bias is self-selection – a sample picked by the departmental manager to 'prove' he is following the system to the letter; he just hides the records which are incomplete.

Where the auditor finds evidence of a deficiency, eg there is no record where one is called for, he should discuss the occurrence with the auditee. The point of this, however, is not to find out why the deficiency has occurred (although if a reason is suggested it can be noted) and still less to argue whether the system can or cannot be applied in the particular case. All that should be sought from the discussion is agreement that the deficiency exists *for whatever reason*. Since the auditor is dealing with objective evidence, it should not be hard to reach this agreement; the job ticket either has or has not been completed. Above all, lengthy debate about the practicality of following the procedure should be avoided. An investigation of causes of deficiency is altogether a separate process and one which comes after an audit.

At the very least, a quality system will not be perfect at the start and deficiencies identified through internal audits must be expected. They are not an indication that the whole thing does not work; they are a means of effecting real improvements. The internal auditor's work mirrors that of the independent assessors, who expect to see evidence of internal audits identifying deficiencies which are then solved through corrective actions. Too many audit records showing that no problems have been found are probably evidence that the audit work has not been done thoroughly enough.

Audit Reports

Whilst carrying out the work, the auditors should make notes of all their findings and on completion, a written report should be prepared. This does not need to be a lengthy document. One page is usually quite sufficient. The information provided in the report should include:

- The date of the audit.
- Who carried it out.
- The scope of the audit (as discussed, this is decided beforehand).
- A statement of any deficiencies identified during the audit. Since, as we shall discuss, any and every deficiency should lead to a corrective action being raised, all that needs recording on the audit report itself is a cross-reference to the relevant corrective action form, eg 'see Corrective Action Form Number 23'. Such a statement of deficiencies can be labelled 'audit results' and if no deficiencies are found in the audit, the correct entry under results would be 'none'.
- Any further comments or 'observations' which may be useful in either reviewing the working of the quality system or in carrying out future audits in the same area. An example might be:

Staff complain that preparing the records takes far more time than envisaged.

Or:

While the records were completed, it is suspected they were filled in after the event. In the next audit, try and test whether the records are contemporary.

The report should be signed by the auditor and then handed to the management representative for actioning, ie through corrective actions, and filing in an appropriate place. Relevant entries should also be entered in the Register Of Audits to show the audit has been carried out and that a report has been prepared.

Follow-up audits

The purpose of auditing is not just to identify problems but, through the corrective action procedure, to lead to eventual improvements in the quality system and its implementation. The auditors' role, as such, is not to propose solutions to problems, but they do have an additional task of establishing whether satisfactory solutions have been found to deficiencies identified in an initial audit. This is achieved through the process of follow-up audits.

Follow-up audits are carried out if an initial audit uncovers deficiencies. These always lead into the corrective action procedure, resulting in a recommendation for some action to overcome the problem identified. These fall broadly into two groups: a change in procedure, which is appropriate where the problem is essentially system-based (eg data cannot be recorded on a form because there is no space allowed to enter it) or a change in how a procedure is implemented. The second may simply amount to an exhortation for staff to try harder. The purpose of the follow-up audit is to establish whether the deficiency identified in the original audit has been solved or not. The scope of a follow-up audit is, therefore, narrow; the only parts of the quality system audited are those where deficiencies were originally identified. If, in an initial audit of the cutting and bending area, a problem was found in the recording of batch numbers on the job ticket, the re-audit would only focus on whether or not the data was now being adequately recorded.

Follow-up audits presuppose that a full corrective action has been followed with the problem investigated, a solution proposed, a decision made on whether to implement the solution and, where appropriate, that a controlled change in the system has been made. Obviously all this will take time and therefore the re-audit should not be carried out until a suitable time has elapsed since the original audit. What is a suitable time? There can be no general answer; it all depends on the nature of the organisation and the working of its quality system. However, assuming that the solution to the deficiency is a change to the system, the time from initial to follow-up needs to be at least as long as it takes to effect such a change. This includes the corrective action to recommend a change, management agreement to make it and the change procedure itself. In the specimen procedure for audits provided, a period of 45 days is allowed for follow-up audits. In some organisations this period may be unrealistically short.

A report should also be prepared to show the outcome of a follow-up audit (and with entries made in the register of audits to complete the records). The follow-up report can be even more succinct than that of the original audit – all that is necessary is to record whether or not the problem has been dealt with or still exists. This can be expressed as 'complete' (problem solved) or 'incomplete' (not solved).

Where it is found on re-audit that the problem has not been solved and the deficiency still exists, two alternative approaches may be considered and built into the procedures. One is to regard the matter as at end as far as the auditing process is concerned. However, the matter cannot just be left there, since presumably the quality system is not working in this area and some action is essential. This may be brought about through a decision taken at the next management review meeting at which all audit reports, including 'incomplete' follow-up audits, are discussed. Alternatively, a corrective action can be raised as a result of the follow-up audit and a further follow-up audit repeated. This cycle can be repeated until the problem is finally solved. (Everyone, by this time, will be so weary of the whole business that a solution will certainly be found.)

We conclude our discussion of auditing and auditors with a specimen procedure which, with fine-tuning, might be incorporated into most companies' quality systems. It will be seen that the auditors' report is prepared after a review meeting with the management representative during which any corrective action forms required are issued. The main purpose of this is to tie into the specimen corrective action procedure we provide later. Auditors, however, will generally find it useful to discuss the outcome of an audit before preparing the formal report.

PROCEDURE SA 9.3

Title	Internal Quality Audits
Purpose	To define procedures relevant to internal auditing of the Quality System.
Scope	All of the Quality System.
References	Quality Manual Procedure Manual: SA 9.4
Definitions	*Internal Quality Audit* Establishing compliance with the Quality System through the activities of members of the Company's staff independent of the area under review.
Documentation	Audit Plan: SA 9.3.2/1 Register Of Audits: SA 9.3.3/1 Audit Report Form: SA 9.3.4/1 Follow-up Audit Report: SA 9.3.5/1

Procedures

SA 9.3.1   *Internal Quality Audit Team*
The Management Representative shall appoint staff to act as Internal Quality Auditors (IQA)
    The IQA shall include a minimum of two.
    The Management Representative may act as an IQA.
    The Management Representative shall ensure the IQA are adequately trained and shall prepare and file records of this training.

SA 9.3.2   *Frequency And Coverage Of Audits*
At least one audit shall be carried out in each quarter of the year.
    Over a year all parts of the Quality system shall be audited at least once.
    In January of each year the Management Representative shall prepare an Audit Plan – SA 9.3.2/1 – for the whole year.

SA 9.3.3   *IQA Meetings*
Before each audit, the Management Representative shall convene a meeting of IQA to:
    Assign audits to the audit team or individual auditors, by reference to specific elements of the Quality System.
    The audits shall be numbered sequentially with the relevant details recorded in the Register Of Audits – SA 9.3.3/1
    Review progress of audits during the current year-to-date.
    Assess IQA performance and review training needs.

Figure 10.1 Specimen procedure

SA 9.3.4   *Audit Work*

On receipt of an audit assignment, the IQA shall review the records of any relevant previous audits carried out within the preceding two years and consider any implications of these for the planned audit.

An appropriate audit checklist shall be prepared by the IQA in advance of the audit.

The IQA shall arrange convenient times for the audit with staff involved in the working areas to be covered in the audit.

The IQA shall then carry out the audit and discuss the results with the Management Representative and the staff covered by the audit.

Where appropriate the Management Representative shall issue Corrective Action Forms – see SA 9.4.

The IQA shall then prepare a report of the audit using the form SA 9.3.4/1 and give this to the Management Representative along with any appropriately completed Corrective Action Forms raised as a result of the audit.

The Management Representative shall make relevant entries in the Register of Audits SA 9.3.3/1, file the audit report and where appropriate follow the Corrective Action Procedures – see SA 9.4.

SA 9.3.5   *Follow-up Audits*

If a Corrective Action is raised as a result of an audit, the Management Representative shall assign the IQA to carry out a follow-up audit within 45 days of the date of the original audit.

The purpose of such follow-up audits shall be to establish the results achieved for each Corrective Action raised by the original audit.

On completion of a follow-up audit, the IQA shall prepare a Follow Up Audit Report – SA 9.3.5/1 – and pass this to the Management Representative who shall make appropriate entries in the Register Of Audits SA 9.3.3/1.

Figure 10.1 Specimen procedure (*cont*)

SA 9.3.2/1 AUDIT PLAN

AUDIT NO	PLANNED DATE	SCOPE

Figure 10.1 Specimen procedure (*cont*)

SA 9.3.3/1   **REGISTER OF AUDITS**

Audit No	Date Started	Scope of Audit	Auditor	Date Report Received	Date Follow-up Audit

Figure 10.1 Specimen procedure (*cont*)

SA 9.3.4/1   **AUDIT REPORT**

Audit No: _____   Date of Audit: _____   Date of Report: _____

SCOPE:

Findings - As per Corrective Action Form Numbers:

_____

NOTES:

Signed: _____ (Auditor)

Figure 10.1 Specimen procedure (*cont*)

SA 9.3.5/1   **FOLLOW-UP AUDIT REPORT**

Audit No _____   Date of
                     Follow-Up Audit _____   Date of Report _____

Corrective Action Form No	Complete	Not Complete

Notes:

Signed _____ (Auditor)

Figure 10.1 Specimen procedure (*cont*)

STAFF TRAINING

Implementing a quality system involves everyone and so before the start-up day all staff must be trained. The most important training for each member of staff is in following the procedures which affect their day-to-day work. If, however, staff were closely involved in developing these procedures, and we argued in chapter 8 that they must be so involved, they will already have a good understanding of what will be required of them. As part of the procedure developing process, they may well have already read the procedures in a draft form. Therefore, training staff in 'their own' procedures should be relatively simple. However, all staff need a fuller understanding of the quality system beyond knowing how to follow the procedures of their own jobs.

The depth of understanding of the quality system needed will not be uniform throughout a company. The senior management should understand most of the system in detail (or how else can they participate in management reviews?). Junior managers should also have a full understanding, but perhaps to a lower level of detail, apart from areas that directly affect them day-to-day. Other staff, of course, have to understand how to work the procedures which cover their specific jobs, but they also need a broader understanding of what lies behind and beyond the bit of the system that affects them directly. Partly this is a matter of motivation; it is easier to follow rules whose purpose is understood than those which appear as mere whims of management. As well, however, all staff will become involved in procedures beyond those covering their normal jobs. Examples include auditing (why are these people checking up on me?) and corrective actions (what have I done wrong this time?). Also, the staff of a particular area are affected by the procedures of upstream or downstream processes.

As a minimum, we recommend that quality system training for all staff should cover the following:

- Why a formal quality system is being introduced and why BS 5750 is thought to be worth all the effort.
- The involvement of all staff in the quality system and that participation is central to the business from now on. The unacceptability of the excuse, 'I haven't time to follow the procedures'.
- The overall quality policy of the company. This will by now be in a written form and copies should be displayed around the company (including in reception for the benefit of visitors). The policy should also be explained to staff, who should be encouraged to think what the policy means to them in practice. Incidentally, during an assessment, individual staff may well be asked to state the company quality policy. They do not have to be able to recite it word for word but should be able to say, in their own words, what it means.

- The documents making up the system with the emphasis on the procedure manual and its accessibility to staff (where the manuals are kept).
- What procedures mean in general – 'everyone singing off the same sheet'.
- The layout of the whole procedure manual – the role of each group of procedures and how they hang together.
- Using forms or other records built into the quality system. The forms used by particular work groups, day to day, need to be discussed in some detail.
- The role of internal auditors.
- Corrective actions including the accessibility of this procedure to all staff (see below).
- What assessment for BS 5750 will involve.

While these topics should be covered in meetings with all staff, they may have to be expressed in different ways to suit individual audiences. In a small company, general topics might be covered at one or two full meetings, followed by smaller work group meetings to focus in detail on relevant procedures and quality records.

Clearly, training meetings to cover the necessary ground will need careful planning and timetabling. This includes assigning tasks to selected training leaders who almost certainly will need some training themselves in the quality system.

As part of the training period, it is vital that staff read for themselves the procedures which affect their day-to-day work. This can present practical problems because, as we discussed in the previous chapter, the number of controlled copies of the procedure manual should be strictly limited and certainly not one per person. Furthermore, there is the important principle that other, uncontrolled copies of a manual must not be 'in use' within an organisation. One solution is that with training spread over one or two weeks prior to the start-up day, there should be time for each department's controlled copy of the manual to be read by all members of staff in turn. Also, it can be reasonably argued that prior to implementation all the documentation is still at 'draft' stage and so *for training purposes only* it is acceptable for additional copies of the manual or parts of it to be made (since the system has not yet been implemented these 'uncontrolled' copies are not 'in use'). Needless to say, such copies should be withdrawn and destroyed by the start-up day.

In a smaller company, one person is often the project leader, chief author of the procedures, organiser of the training and also takes on the role of management representative. Even though staff have, hopefully, been involved throughout, he will come to be regarded as the ultimate authority on the quality system and its implementation. A practical consequence is that during training and afterwards he will be asked to explain, elaborate or resolve inconsistencies in the written procedures. As far as possible, staff should be told to follow the procedures as they are set down in the manuals and no interpretation should be given, even by the author of the documents. The reason for this is that once procedures are elaborated in this way, they exist in multiple versions – the written version and the interpreted version available to the group who consulted the authority – and *there is no longer a common set of procedures throughout the company*. Of course, despite all efforts, some procedures will be ambiguous, unclear or difficult to apply in circumstances which the authors did not foresee. The solution is to change them through the change procedure, after the problem has been identified and investigated by a corrective action. The latter may follow from an audit or arise from the initiative of the individual staff identifying the problem.

START-UP

The only major issue to be decided about start-up is 'big bang' or 'roll-out'.

With 'big bang' the quality system starts throughout the company at one time, eg nine o'clock on Monday, 1 September. Everyone in all departments is then expected to comply with the quality system. The advantages of this approach is that it is all clear-cut; there should be no uncertainty about the matter. Furthermore, compared with 'roll-out', 'big bang' usually provides a shorter route to assessment and therefore gaining BS 5750, the culmination of the project. The major disadvantages of 'big bang' are the disruption and demands on the management representative. The disruption may be such that for the first week or so, all the attention of the company may be on the formal side of following the new system to the neglect of day-to-day business. There is no point gaining BS 5750 if its implementation so distracts from revenue-earning activities that the future of the business is threatened. However, this would be an extreme situation and probably reflect that the system had not been thought out well in the first place.

In the period after a 'big bang' start-up, the management representative will be very much involved in seeing that the system is working, and the initial demands on his time will be considerable. If, as is common in smaller businesses, the management representative combines this role with other critical activities, the pressure can be too much.

If the 'big bang' approach is followed (and in the authors' opinion, it is often the better approach), 'Quality Day' should be made a big event. Advance publicity as well as training should leave staff in no doubt about the date or its importance. On the day, the chief executive or chairman may make a short speech reinforcing the benefits to be obtained from the new system and the requirement for company-wide involvement. Depending on the culture of the company, badges, posters, balloons or other gimmicks might all be useful to dramatise the event. The company's quality policy should by now be displayed around the premises.

The 'roll-out' approach to start-up is to introduce the quality system in only one or two departments and then extend it to others until the whole company is covered. This approach may overcome problems of disruption and excessive demands on the management representative that can be experienced with 'big bang'. Furthermore, the quality system can be tried out in less (or more) problematical areas. Experience is in this way built up before involving the whole company. The disadvantages are that the period to assessment may be lengthened, confusion may be created about the company's commitment to the quality system and there may be problems of interface. It is all very well saying that one department only will initially follow the quality system, but in practice departments are usually closely interlinked. Following a set of procedures in one department may, for, example, require actions in upstream departments. In the coat-hanger factory example, the finishing department cannot make entries on the job ticket if it is not available because the cutting and bending department have not yet implemented the quality system.

In some types of business a problem found on start-up, regardless of whether the approach is 'big bang' or 'roll out', is that jobs are in-process at the time the quality system is implemented. The choice is usually between applying the new system only to jobs started after start-up or to jobs as they enter each department. The former approach is the better one where the whole process-cycle is reasonably short, while the latter may be better where it is long (otherwise processes well downstream may not be in a position to follow the system for quite some time and the time to assessment can be lengthened as a consequence). Either way, the rule must be clear and known throughout the company.

A final point about start-up: begin auditing very soon afterwards. Only through the audit process can a judgement be made about the effectiveness of the system. It is not enough that the system is 'generally going well'. Following a quality system involves attending to all the details. Evaluation of initial effectiveness requires the disciplined approach of the audit.

WHEN THINGS GO WRONG

No quality system is perfect, especially at the beginning. So it is to be expected that problems will be found in using the system immediately after implementation. Even if the system is near perfect to begin with, in the long run adaptation to a changing environment will become necessary; in a coat-hanger factory, new materials may be introduced which the original process procedures simply do not cover. Furthermore, even if it could be perfect, the system has to be implemented by fallible human beings and in practice this is usually the source of most problems. These may be particularly acute at the start when, despite training, familiarity with the system is less than complete. Even once the initial learning curve is climbed, problems and mistakes of human error will occur forever. To deal with all these problems, the quality system must have a built-in mechanism and this is a formal requirement of the Standard (*4.14 Correctve Action* of BS 5750 Part 1). Corrective actions provide the means of solving quality system problems.

The mechanism of corrective action involves four stages:

1. Identification of the problem.
2. Investigation and recommendation of a solution.
3. The decision on whether to implement this recommendation.
4. As appropriate, either system change or improved implementation.

We will discuss each stage in turn. We also provide a specimen procedure for corrective action.

In chapter 9 we briefly mentioned the sources of quality system problem identification (see Figure 9.3). The internal audit process will inevitably identify deficiencies and problems in the operation of the quality system and at the start most corrective actions will be initiated by the internal audit team through their work. Later, when the system is examined by independent assessors, they too will also identify deficiencies (also called 'non-conformities') and expect these to be addressed through the corrective action procedure. However, in an effective quality system, problem identification is not solely the province of the quality 'professionals'. Anyone within a company who understands the quality system's purpose – and this should be everyone – is in a position to identify problems in its working or identify quality problems in the processes. Since the quality system is meant to address all sources of these problems, to identify a process problem – defective coat-hangers etc – is to identify a quality system problem. Who is better placed to spot problems in a process than those working on it day after day?

Another aspect of access to the corrective action procedure for all staff is that it can offer a means of de-personalising issues. The problem may be that Joe is not giving Fred adequate job instructions and all too often this sort of thing can blow up into a major clash. With a corrective action procedure operating, Joe now simply reports that the prescribed job instructions are not being passed to him and this is then investigated as a quality system (rather than Joe v Fred) problem. Once the quality system is bedded-in, therefore, it is a healthy sign for a range of staff to initiate the corrective action procedure.

Another means of problem identification is customer (or possibly supplier) complaint. These might arise spontaneously or through a process of actively establishing customers' satisfaction. Either way, it is important that complaints are dealt with at two levels. Firstly, if the customer is unhappy the specific problem must be solved, wherever possible. The customer may well insist on this anyway. If the complaint is that the coat-hangers are misshapen, the first priority is probably to replace the defective products and hopefully this will mollify the customer. However, that the mistake has happened at all, points to a deficiency in the quality system and it is essential to investigate the root causes in order that their recurrence can be prevented. Therefore, through corrective actions, problem solving is no longer just fire-fighting. Instead, permanent solutions to quality problems are found.

Incidentally, a quality system should have a formal method (ie procedures) of monitoring customer satisfaction with the service provided by the company. This can take various forms, depending on the nature of the business. Also, some assessors consider that there should be a customer complaint procedure, covering the logging and investigation of such complaints with a feedback to the customer (stating how the problem has been dealt with).

The last source of problem identification is the 'good idea'. The system is working well enough, but someone believes that a change would bring improvement. Such suggestions are a mark of an organisation committed to quality. The fact that an improvement is suggested implies that the existing quality system is in some way less than optimum. 'Good ideas' are, therefore, in effect another method of identifying deficiencies in the widest sense of the term.

Of course, with well-motivated staff, all this problem identification can get a shade out of hand. As part of the corrective action procedure, therefore, it is best to build-in some sort of test to decide that there is a prima-facie case worth going to the trouble of investigating. This can be met by requiring problems and deficiencies to be stated on a special form issued by the management representative, who effectively makes the judgement that the issue is appropriately dealt with through a corrective action.

It is important that the initiator of the corrective action (the person identifying the problem) simply states the problem *and does not suggest the solution*. It may be transparently clear that the reason the hangers were misshapen was because of a fault with the bending machine, but the initial entry on a corrective action record should state the problem, and that alone, so that the causes can be *fully* investigated (perhaps the machine caused the problem, but why were the faulty products not taken out of the line?). The management representative must, therefore, strictly ensure that the initiator confines himself to a statement of the problem rather than jump to the solution.

Once the problem has been identified and recorded, the next step is to have an investigation to determine the cause of the problem and recommend a solution. The management representative must therefore select someone to carry out this work. It is generally better for the corrective action initiator not to be the investigator of the problem. However, an exception is the corrective action arising as a 'good idea'. In this case the separation of initiation and investigation is artificial – the problem only arises because the initiator has a proposed solution. Even so, the management representative may still require an independent investigation before a management decision is made. There is certainly no need for the investigator to be independent of the area where the problem has occurred. On the contrary, often the only staff qualified to identify the causes of the problem and suggest remedies are those closely involved in the process. As we will discuss shortly, the causes of a deficiency may well be how it is implemented rather than a fault in the procedure itself. This situation may be obvious to the management representative at the outset and he may decide that the best investigator is the person having difficulty following the procedure. This can be a very practical approach, but beware: corrective actions are not, and must not be seen as, disciplinary devices against staff not complying with the system. If staff wilfully choose not to follow the system, then sooner or later disciplinary measures may be needed but, as such, they are not part of the quality system.

Something which the investigator must recognise is that deficiencies do not necessarily imply system faults. The procedure may be perfectly reasonable and workable but because of inadequate training, or for whatever reason, the staff concerned are not following the procedure. Initially, many problems of this sort will be found. The first task of an investigation, therefore, is to establish whether the deficiency is system-related or people-related (occasionally, the problem may be of both sorts). Where it arises from the system, the recommendation will be in terms of changing the system, whereas where people are the problem, the solution is likely to be in terms of retraining. In practice, the investigation may itself solve a people problem: Nelly was not following the procedure because she did not know she had to; she now knows and from now on she will do it. In such a case, while the formality of a management decision will still be needed after the investigation (since this is a step in a formal procedure), it may amount to no more than noting that the problem's solution is in hand.

Once the investigation is complete, an appropriate management decision is needed to implement a solution. Again, this may involve a change in the system through the change procedure (see chapter 9) or involve staff training in how to implement the procedure. Either type of decision might be taken at a full management review meeting or by someone acting for the management – usually the management representative. When a decision is to be referred or when it is to be acted on by the management representative alone might depend on how fundamental the change is and, frankly, the degree of confidence placed in the management representative. In the specimen procedure which follows, the management representative can decide whether to implement the recommendation of the investigator on his own initiative or whether to refer the matter. In some organisations it may be considered that this gives the management representative too much power. However, in most organisations it will be found impractical to defer all decisions until they have been considered at relatively infrequent meetings, particularly where the issue is one

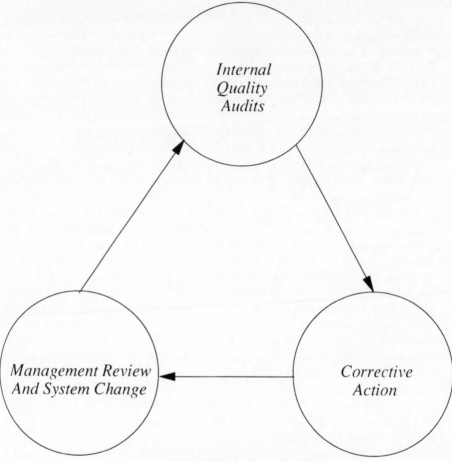

Figure 10.2 The quality triad

of implementation rather than change. Whoever is authorised to make a decision does not have to be bound by the solution recommended by the investigator. Another and better solution may suggest itself.

Whether the outcome of the corrective action is a change in procedure or in how it is implemented, the management and staff of the department concerned must be consulted. Implementation through retraining or encouragement can only be achieved within the work area concerned and if a change in the department's procedure is envisaged, it would be foolish not to involve them. Without this involvement, there is a good chance that the procedure would still not be appropriate or not implemented because it is not 'owned'.

If the outcome of the corrective action is a decision to change the system, this must be done through the formal change procedure, with possibly a definite timetable being set, probably within the period allowed for the follow-up audit (as discussed earlier). Indeed, as we discussed in the previous chapter, change procedures and corrective actions are locked together; change can only be initiated through following the corrective action procedure. Figure 10.2 reproduces the 'Quality triad' concept first illustrated in chapter 2. Problems are identified and investigated through corrective action, management review decides on action and, if necessary, implements changes, and internal audits establish whether the problem has been solved. If a problem is still apparent, the cycle goes through corrective actions again until it is solved for good. The three elements in the triad not only ensure that the quality system is effective but, used correctly, lead to a continual process of improvement.

We conclude this chapter with a specimen corrective action procedure which is probably adaptable to most smaller organisations. As with all formal procedures, a facility for records of compliance is built in. In the specimen, these take the form of a corrective action register and sequentially numbered corrective action forms. The latter record a statement of the deficiency, the results of the investigation and recommendations made, the management decision and, if relevant, the date changes are made to the quality system (through the change procedures). Details of the staff involved are also recorded on the form. The same information could, of course, be kept in a different way.

PROCEDURE SA 9.4

Title   Corrective Action

Purpose   To define procedures relevant to determining the causes of
any deficiencies in the Quality System and its
implementation, and consider what should be done to
remedy such deficiencies.

Scope   All of the Quality System.

References   Quality Manual
Procedure Manual: SA 9.1 SA 9.2

Definitions   *Customer Complaint* Negative or unfavourable comments of
a specific and substantial content, on the performance of the
Company's services made in any form, by a customer.

Documentation   Corrective Action Form: SA 9.4.1/1
Corrective Action Register: SA 9.4.2/1

Procedures

SA 9.4.1   *Initiation Of A Corrective Action*
Any member of staff identifying a deficiency in the Quality
System or its implementation or receiving a customer
complaint shall initiate a Corrective Action by requesting a
Corrective Action Form – SA 9.4.1/1 from the Management
Representative.

SA 9.4.2   *Issue Of A Corrective Action Form*
On receiving a request as above, the Management
Representative, if he considers the action to be appropriate,
shall issue to the initiator a Corrective Action Form – SA
9.4.1/1 which shall have a number written on it to correspond
to the next sequential form number in the Corrective Action
Register – SA 9.4.2/1.
The Management Representative shall on issuing a
Corrective Action Form – SA 9.4.1/1 – make appropriate
entries in the Corrective Action Register – SA 9.4.2/1.

SA 9.4.3   *Statement Of Deficiency*
The initiator shall complete the relevant part of the
Corrective Action Form – SA 9.4.1/1 – and state the nature
of the deficiency.
The initiator shall return the Form to the Management
Representative who shall make appropriate entries in the
Corrective Action Register – SA 9.4.2/1.

Figure 10.3 Specimen procedure

SA 9.4.4   *Investigation Of The Deficiency*
The Management Representative shall appoint a member of
staff he considers suitable to investigate the causes of the
deficiency and make a recommendation on whether a change
to the Quality System is required and if so the nature of the
change. The investigator may also or instead make a
recommendation on the implementation of the Quality
System including any requirement for staff training.

The Management Representative shall pass to the
investigator the relevant Corrective Action Form – SA
9.4.1/1 and make appropriate entries in the Corrective
Action Register – SA 9.4.2/1.

The investigator shall record the results of the investigation
on the Corrective Action Form – SA 9.4.1/1 – and pass the
Form with the relevant parts completed to the Management
Representative.

SA 9.4.5   *Referral Or Action By The Management Representative*
The Management Representative, as he considers
appropriate, shall either take action in relation to the
Corrective Action or refer the matter to the next
Management Review Meeting (see SA 9.1).

In either case, the decision shall be recorded on the
Corrective Action Form – SA 9.4.1/1 and in the Corrective
Action Register – SA 9.4.2/1.

SA 9.4.6   *Management Decision*
The Management Representative or a Management Review
Meeting shall then review the Corrective Action and decide:
  To make changes to the Quality System either as
  proposed by the investigator or otherwise and set a
  timetable for making the change. Such a change shall be
  made through the Document Control procedure – SA
  9.2
Or
  To make no change to the Quality System but, if
  appropriate, take action on the implementation of the
  Quality System with due regard for any training
  requirements.
The Management Representative shall record this decision
on the relevant Corrective Action Form – SA 9.4.1/1 – and in
the Corrective Action Register – SA 9.4.2/1.

Figure 10.3 Specimen procedure (*cont*)

SA 9.4.1/1   **CORRECTIVE ACTION FORM**   Form No: _____

1.   Statement of Deficiency

_____

_____

_____

Signed: _____ (Person Reporting Deficiency)   Date: _____

2.   Investigation Report

_____

_____

_____

Signed: _____ (Investigator)   Date: _____

3.   Referral/Management Representative Action

     Referral | | MR Action | |

4.   Procedural Change Decision

Implement Investigator's Recommendations ( )   No Change ( )

Other Changes - As Below

_____

_____

5.   Date of Change Implementation (If Relevant) _____

Figure 10.3 Specimen procedure (*cont*)

SA 9.4.2/1   CORRECTIVE ACTION REGISTER

FORM NO	DATE ISSUED	ISSUED TO	BRIEF DESCRIPTION OF DEFICIENCY	DATE RETURNED	INVESTIGATOR	DATE TO INVESTIGATE	DATE RETURNED	REFERRAL/ MR ACTION	PROCEDURE CHANGE DECISION	DATE OF IMPLEMENTATION (If Relevant)

Figure 10.3 Specimen procedure (*cont*)

11   ASSESSMENT

The culmination of a BS 5750 project is successful assessment. In this chapter we cover the choice of assessor, bedding-in the system and what assessment involves.

CHOICE OF ASSESSOR

To become registered to BS 5750, a company must have its quality system successfully assessed by an independent certification body. These bodies fall into two groups: those which have been accredited by the National Accreditation Council For Certification Bodies (NACCB) and others who have not been accredited in this way. In June 1992 there were twenty bodies on the NACCB's list – see Appendix 3 (since the list continues to grow it is worth contacting the NACCB for an up-to-date version). In principle (and also, sadly, in practice) anyone can set themselves up as an assessment body and hand out BS 5750 certificates. However, accredited assessors are rigorously checked and regularly monitored by the NACCB. Furthermore, accreditation is only for specific industry sectors where experience and competence can be demonstrated (known as a the 'scope' of accreditation).

At the time of writing, companies granted BS 5750 by a NACCB-accredited body for the relevant activity are indicated in bold type in the DTI's List Of Registered Companies, while companies assessed by non-accredited bodies have an entry in standard type. In 1993, however, the DTI intends to include in the List *only* companies assessed by NACCB-accredited bodies, working within their sector 'scopes'. Since the DTI List is regarded as the definitive statement of who has got or not got BS 5750, there is a strong argument for choosing an assessor with NACCB accreditation for your own activity.

As well as the style of entry in the DTI List, companies assessed by bodies with accreditation in their field of activity are also entitled to use a different version of the BS 5750 mark – the 'crown and tick'. This is illustrated in Figure 11.1.

Accredited for a specific activity

Not accredited

Figure 11.1 Two versions of the BS 5750 mark

A final point about using an accredited or non-accredited assessor is that the choice may not arise because none of the certification bodies may be accredited for your particular activity. This will be the case if your company is a BS 5750 'pioneer'. If no other company in your particular business has sought BS 5750, it is unlikely that any of the assessors will have gone through the NACCB process to be accredited. However, as the coverage of BS 5750 extends, this situation will diminish – the major assessment bodies are constantly extending their accreditation scope into new areas.

NACCB-registered bodies are of two broad types: those offering assessment across a wide range of business activities and the specialists, eg The Quality Scheme For Ready Mixed Concrete. Clearly, if there is a specialist body for your own activity you should consider it, but otherwise it can be ruled out. In practice, therefore, your choice of assessor is between any of those bodies who are willing to carry out an assessment in your area of activity (at least three of them will cover *all* fields). One or more of these assessors may be accredited for your activity.

Regardless of their specialisation, or whether or not they are accredited to the activity, all assessors work in broadly the same way. The assessment itself falls into two stages: an evaluation of the documented quality system to establish whether it meets the requirements of the Standard and an on-site assessment to establish that the system is being followed. However, that is not the end of the matter. BS 5750 is not like passing a driving test; you are not licensed for ever without re-testing. After successful assessment a company is, of course, expected to continue to keep its Quality System working effectively and the selected assessors check that this is done by regular surveillance visits. Some go further and work in a three-year cycle of assessment, surveillance and re-assessment, while others continue with surveillance visits. Either way, the relationship with the assessment body is continuous and long term and this needs to be borne in mind when making the initial selection.

The assessors you use will provide you with a service; assessment and the process of selecting them should be basically no different from choosing any other service supplier with whom you enter a long term contract. You need to be confident that the service offered, in all aspects, will meet your particular requirements and that the costs represent value for money. As in any purchasing situation, this does not mean just going for the cheapest (as we will show shortly, the charges do vary quite widely), but if a more expensive quotation is accepted it should be considered to offer, in some way, additional value. As a first step in making a selection, we suggest that a written enquiry is sent to a number of the NACCB-registered certification bodies; perhaps all that appear to be at all likely to cover your particular field. The enquiry can be a letter covering:

- What you want to be assessed for, ie BS 5750 Part 1 or 2.
- An indication of your timetable, eg 'We intend to implement our quality system on January 1st and would hope to be assessed by late April or early May'.
- A very brief outline of your own company and its field of activity, eg 'We are a specialist provider of market research services, have a staff of around 50 working from one office'.
- A request for information on the assessors' experience in your field and whether they have accreditation for this activity.

The timing of making this initial contact may be critical. Most assessors have a booked-up schedule of assessments and may be unable to start one for a new client within three or more months. Therefore the assessor needs to be selected well before the envisaged assessment date. However, as we will explain shortly, a bedding-in period is certainly needed between the date of implementing the quality system and assessment, and in practice many companies will find that the desirable bedding-in period is longer than the timescale the assessors offer. So around about the implementation date is usually early enough to make the initial enquiries, although there is no harm in doing so earlier – even (as mentioned in chapter 5) right at the start of the project.

Once the enquiries have been sent out, the initiative moves to the assessors and the speed and efficiency with which they respond could be a factor influencing the final choice (why deal with an organisation which appears inefficient or lacking in 'quality' in this respect?). Some of those contacted may respond negatively and state that they do not wish to carry out an assessment of a company in your own business, but otherwise the response is likely to include brochures on the services offered and an application questionnaire to be completed on your own company (to provide the assessor with relevant information in preparing a quotation). There may also be a personalised reply, perhaps addressing the enquiry about accreditation.

After receipt of a completed application questionnaire, the assessor may propose to make a preliminary visit before preparing a quotation. Obviously this allows the firm concerned to obtain a clearer understanding of what the assessment work will involve, but equally it gives you the opportunity to find out about them, including how in detail they carry out assessment work and their experience in the particular field. However, as a matter of policy, at least one of the general scope assessors does not make such preliminary visits to smaller companies (they possibly claim that the resulting savings in their own marketing costs are passed on to clients in lower assessment fees). Whether such a trade-off of lower costs against the more limited opportunity to make a judgement on the likely service to be provided is acceptable, is entirely a matter for the potential client.

The next step in the process will be receipt of formal quotations from the potential assessors. These will set out all the details of the service (eg number of visits for assessment, frequency of surveillance visits, policy on re-assessment), the timing – the earliest date for assessment (there is usually no problem in putting it back) and, not least, the charges and payment terms. Figure 11.2 provides, as an illustration only, the charges (quoted in January 1992) to be levied over three years, quoted by three firms. In this case the client was a professional service company, with a staff of about fifty working from one site only. Obviously quotations will vary widely depending on the size, structure and activities of the businesses to be assessed and, like other costs, may increase as time goes on.

Although the figures in Figure 11.2 give some indication of the scale of charges entailed in assessment for a smaller company, the point of interest is the very wide variation in quotations. Clearly it is prudent to approach several potential assessors.

Assessor	Year 1 £	Year 2 £	Year 3 £	Total – 3 Years £
A	1500	700	700	2900
B	3750	1100	550	5400
C	3925	1600	1600	7125

Notes: A – No pre-quotation visit offered.

B – An alternative payment option averaged the annual charges over the three years.

C – Unlike B whose cycle of charges would be repeated in year four onwards, C would continue indefinitely to charge £1600 for annual surveillance.

Figure 11.2 Assessment quotation illustration (January 1992)

BEDDING-IN

It is unrealistic to expect the quality system to work perfectly or even satisfactorily from the first day. There will certainly be defects in the design of the system – parts which either do not work well or do not work at all. Equally, despite all the training, staff will find initial difficulties in following the system. Some will take time to come to terms with a formal quality system, including the important principle that even a bad procedure has to be followed until it has been changed. Bearing everything in mind, very few companies are likely to feel confident enough in their system to seek an immediate assessment.

There is also another consideration. The assessment will be mainly based on objective evidence of compliance with the quality system – the quality records which, at the point of start-up, are non-existent. Only as the processes of the company are carried out and the procedures followed are the quality records built up. A period needs to elapse, therefore, before the assessors can feel confident that compliance with the quality system can be demonstrated. The length of time needed to build up adequate records will depend on the nature of the businesses. A repetitive manufacturing process turning out hundreds of a standard product each week is clearly, in this respect, very different from a project-based business with job timescales of two or three months.

Taking into account both the need to fine-tune the system and its implementation and the need to build up sufficient records, probably very few companies are likely to seek an assessment in less than three months from start-up and many will wish to have a bedding-in period of six to nine months. Generally, such timescales fit in well with the availability of assessors' staff for the work. Furthermore, bedding-in periods of three months or more are thought appropriate by most assessment bodies; at least one will not consider an assessment in any shorter period.

The bedding-in period is emphatically not just dead waiting-time. It is the period when the system is really made to work and starts to produce some internal benefits. The key tool to achieve this is the quality triad: auditing to monitor compliance, corrective action to investigate problems and recommend solutions, and management review to decide on and implement change. The start of this cycle is the internal audit process described in the previous chapter. Auditing, therefore, must be carried out throughout the bedding-in period to identify problems and find solutions. The sooner this process starts the better, and the frequency of audit at this time should be higher than planned in 'normal' times. If possible, before assessment the whole system and its implementation should have been audited at least once.

There is also another point about auditing during the bedding-in period. Since the assessors are in effect external auditors, internal auditing helps prepare the company and its staff. If the auditors are doing their work well, their activities will be broadly similar to that of the external assessors – examining quality records, observing staff at work and asking questions.

The main evidence sought by either internal auditors or assessors is from quality records. Attention should, therefore, be focused during the bedding-in period (and ever afterwards) on both keeping correct records and on their filing and safekeeping. As described in chapter 9, there should be a specific procedure controlling quality records, and internal auditing should cover this part of the system, along with all other system control procedures (including the auditing of the audit procedure itself).

As well as auditing, the other system control procedures should be followed throughout the bedding-in period; do not wait before starting these. Obviously, the audit procedure will generate corrective actions and, apart from the matters dealt with by the management representative alone, this will lead to the need for management reviews. However, irrespective of the need to discuss corrective actions, management reviews need to be held regularly to discuss the workings of the quality system during (and after) the bedding-in period. Cutting out all the BS jargon, this amounts to a company's senior staff considering the progress of a major project and making decisions to correct any problems.

As part of reviews during bedding-in, controlled changes will almost certainly be needed to the quality system. Faulty procedures will need redrafting and possibly new procedures adding. The formal approach to system control and change was discussed in chapter 9. An additional point, however, is that staff training must cover changes to the system – it must be ongoing. It is no good making a necessary change to the system if staff are not kept informed. They cannot do what they do not know. Often this may, in practice, amount to no more than telling relevant staff that a change has been made and where in the procedures to find it. Arguably, it is not a good idea to paraphrase the modified procedure; staff should *read* it in full in a controlled copy of the procedure manual (which, when the change has been made, will contain the new version of the procedure, with the revision probably highlighted in some way).

Ideally, the bedding-in period should last until the company is confident that the quality system is working well and is being followed in all but the most exceptional and occasional circumstances. Then, and only then, should assessment be sought. However, in practice, since most companies will want to achieve BS 5750 sooner rather than later and since the assessment has to be booked well in advance, a judgement will have to be made that the company will be ready for assessment by a certain, forward date. It is much easier to fix this date after at least some of the bedding-in period has elapsed and experience of the system's operation has been built up.

Before final assessment, some companies consider it worthwhile to have a 'pre-audit assessment' carried out. Some of the assessment bodies offer this as an additional service and other consultancies are also available for the work. If a consultant was used in developing the system, some form of this work may be offered as part of the overall package. Such pre-assessment audits are, in effect, dress rehearsals for the real thing and allow problems to be corrected rather than allowing them to be identified as 'non-conformities' at assessment – possibly leading to an initial failure to achieve BS 5750. Apart from possible delays in the whole process, and the additional costs entailed, it is hard to argue a case against pre-audit assessment. However, the cost of this service may be quite substantial in relation to the whole cost of assessment; if the assessors themselves are carrying out the work, they are likely to charge at much the same rate as when carrying out a full-blown assessment. Also, most of any problems likely to be identified during a pre-assessment audit should be spotted as part of normal internal auditing. Arguably, the money spent on pre-assessment auditing might be better allocated to internal auditor training, where the benefits are long-term.

However, we recognise that any company designing and implementing a quality system on an entirely do-it-yourself basis will feel very vulnerable going into assessment if no outsider has critically reviewed the system. As we discussed in chapter 4, consultancy can be bought-in in small time-blocks and there is a strong argument, in this situation, for using an outside consultant to vet the system and its operation prior to assessment. This might be best done in two bites: a review of the documented system on or just before implementation, followed by the consultant carrying out an in-house audit some time after implementation. This mirrors the methods of external assessors.

THE DESK INVESTIGATION

As we mentioned earlier, the assessment takes place in two stages. The first is concerned with establishing whether the documented quality system meets the requirements of the Standard, leaving to later the question of whether the system is actually being followed. This first stage, commonly referred to as the *desk investigation,* usually takes place well before the on-site assessment (eg if the assessment is booked for three months hence, the desk investigation may take place six weeks before the on-site assessment).

The practices of different assessment firms vary, but commonly, desk investigation is carried out off-site at the assessors' office. Soon after a formal application, the company seeking assessment will be asked to provide copies of all the quality documentation – the quality and procedure manuals – and it is on this evidence alone that conformity of the system with the Standard is judged. In requesting copies of the documents, the assessors may make clear whether they require these to be controlled or up-to-date, but uncontrolled, copies. If they do not make this clear, the point should be clarified. It is a nice debating point whether documentation sent to a third party can any longer be regarded as controlled; what happens if changes to the system are made whilst a copy of the documentation is outside the control of the company? It clearly cannot be changed and updated as the system prescribes.

In a desk investigation, the assessors need to establish whether the requirements of the Standard are being addressed and, if so, whether the procedures in place provide a practical means of achieving this. The two questions are distinct. If a company is seeking registration to BS 5750 Part 1, its quality system must include reference to design control. If this requirement has not been addressed at all, then clearly there can be no possibility, as things stand, that BS 5750 Part 1 can be awarded. However, in addition, the system must include practical methods of ensuring that design control is exercised in day-to-day activities. In our approach to the documented system, we recommended a clear separation consisting of a quality manual made up of policy statements on how each requirement of the Standard will be addressed, with cross-references to a separate procedure manual. The latter provides the practical means of carrying out the policy. This structure enables the assessor to carry out the desk investigation efficiently. The manual provides the bridge between the Standard and the company's quality policies and leads easily into the procedure manual. Without any familiarity with the particular business, the assessor, as a result, can understand the particular quality system and evaluate its coverage against what is required.

There are really only two outcomes of the desk investigation: either the documented quality system is judged to meet the requirements of the Standard, or it is not. True, in the former case there might be some points of detail which the assessor questions or is unclear about and these will be raised prior to site assessment. However, it can be assumed in this case that the assessors expect that any such problems can be resolved either before the site visit or soon afterwards, and that in themselves they are not so serious as to make it impossible to award BS 5750. On the other hand, where the assessor believes that one or more requirements of the Standard are not met or adequately addressed by the quality system, there will be failure on these grounds alone. In such circumstances a site assessment would serve no purpose until a major revision of the quality system has been completed. How this situation is handled, and the implications in terms of additional charges, varies between assessors. However, the procedure that is followed should be known in advance of the assessment. Indeed it is an aspect of the service provided which should be clarified before the assessor is chosen and the contract signed. Whatever the practice, if this situation occurs it should, at worse, only be a set-back to the timetable for gaining BS 5750. The identified problem can be dealt with through a change in the system, the desk investigation then completed satisfactorily and the postponed on-site assessment arranged.

Where the outcome of the desk investigation is unfavourable, most companies will not feel in a position to argue the matter. However, in some circumstances – especially where the assessor is unfamiliar with a particular business – there can be legitimate doubts about how the Standard should be applied in the particular circumstances. An example could be meeting the requirement *4.11 Inspection, measuring and test equipment* of BS 5750 Part 1 in a professional service company. The application of this requirement will be a long way from the common practice in manufacturing. It may be that a view has been taken that the need to apply this requirement simply does not arise, given the nature of the business. In cases such as this, it may be difficult to arrive at a clear-cut view and both assessor and company should expect to discuss and debate the matter before a final, and possibly adverse, decision is made on the basis of the desk investigation. As a last resort, the contract with the assessor will include some sort of appeals procedure which can be followed if the company strongly believes in its own interpretation of the Standard. However, most will probably bend the knee with the best grace they can and make such changes to the quality system as the assessor believes appropriate.

Where, as a result of the desk investigation, minor questions are raised, these should be carefully considered and changes instigated before the on-site assessment. Remember, however, that in making any such changes the formal change procedure must be followed. This involves initiating corrective actions leading, if appropriate, through management review to a controlled change of the system.

ON-SITE ASSESSMENT

For a smaller company, the on-site assessment typically involves one or two of the assessor staff and takes up about two days. Obviously, this will vary according to both the overall size and the number of operating sites of the company being assessed. The purpose of this part of the assessment is to establish whether the company is following its own quality system; the desk investigation will have determined whether the system itself meets the Standard. The assessment work is, in principle, exactly the same as an internal audit. The assessor uses the documented system – especially the procedure manual – to establish what *ought* to happen at a specific point in a process and seeks evidence that this is what does happen in practice. There should rarely be any grey areas; either a particular requirement is being followed or it is not. Also, as in an internal audit, the primary evidence sought is from objective quality records and much of the assessors' time will be spent in examining these. However, the assessors can also observe whether staff's activities are in conformity with the procedures. If, for example, the procedures require an entry to be made on a job ticket as the batch leaves a department, observation may show whether this is being done or the records are being (wrongly) created after the event. Also, the assessor may ask staff to describe how a certain process is carried out with the purpose of establishing familiarity with relevant procedures. If the staff do not know what the quality system requires of them, how can the company be regarded as following its own system? This, however, does not mean that staff are expected to be able to recite procedures word-perfect.

An important issue is what special preparation should be made immediately before the assessors' visit. The 'correct' answer is none. The staff should be fully trained in the operation of the quality system and really no more can be done. However, in practice, most companies will make that special extra effort in the lead-up to the big day with particular attention to meticulous and retrievable records. The staff are also likely to receive coaching in how to handle auditors. A practical tip here is that if, during an assessment, staff are asked a question about a particular activity, the answer sought is in terms of procedures rather than the fundamental principles of wire-bending or what-ever. If the employee is unsure of the correct 'procedural' answer to the question, the best response might be:

> I am not quite sure what we do in these circumstances so I would look up the relevant procedure in the manual or consult my manager.

Another tip is to discourage staff from starting the sort of rambling discourse that can result in 'self-conviction', eg:

> How do we set the machine? Oh well, the procedure is . . . (etc etc) Well, that is what we are supposed to do, but of course what we really do is take out this old notebook of mine I've had for years and this tells me how to do it. To make things right, we enter up the setting records on the proper form when the machine is running. Another thing is . . .

Staff, at all levels, should be told to answer assessors' questions as best they can, succinctly, and then say no more until another question is asked.

Most companies will undertake some such last-minute coaching, but realistically its effects will be, at most, very marginal. If you have only paid lip-service to your own quality system up to this point, things will not be put right in a few days. Also, there are dangers in making staff over-anxious. With a good quality system in place, nobody should need to feel that the future of the company hangs on their responses to an assessor.

Before arriving, the assessors will probably indicate their proposed schedule and timetable. Relevant staff will clearly have to be available when each department is visited as an assessment of the marketing department cannot be carried out if the staff are all out seeing customers. This is a case where some disruption to routine business may have to be accepted. Normally, the key contact between the company and the assessors is the management representative (or whoever has that role). Indeed, this member of staff should expect to give all his time to the assessment visit. Apart from direct discussions about the system in general and the aspects of direct concern to him (eg the system control procedures, such as auditing and corrective action), the management representative normally accompanies the assessors throughout their visit, takes them to each department and introduces them to staff. Also, very few management representatives would not want to be present at all times as the assessment work is carried out. With probably the best knowledge of the quality system in the company, the management representative should be able to help the assessor interpret evidence in the best possible light!

The assessors will normally cover the whole company and the operation of all the quality system. It is very unlikely that no problem at all will be found and a single deficiency, or even quite a few, does not have to result in failure. A basic distinction is made between major and minor deficiencies (or non-conformities). A major deficiency is one where a significant part of a quality system or a set of procedures is not being followed at all; for example, no quality records are kept for the cutting and bending department of the coat-hanger works or there is no effective control over system documents with different versions of manuals in use. If such situations are found by the assessor, the company will fail BS 5750. Failure of this sort should hardly be a shock, however. Auditing and management review ought to have identified these problems before assessment and the date put back. This would have been far better than to fail.

Examples of minor non-conformities include entries missing from some job tickets, or a failure to label some design plans or occasionally overlooking a checking procedure. Where problems such as these are found, the assessor effectively logs 'penalty points' against the company. If the total of such minor non-conformities is above some level, BS 5750 will not be awarded, but otherwise a pass can still be given. Unfortunately, it is not possible to state precisely how many minor non-conformities are treated as acceptable; certainly, at double figures the situation may start to become doubtful.

The precise procedure followed in cases where BS 5750 is not awarded at the first attempt varies between assessment bodies and should be understood before a commitment is made (ie at any initial, pre-proposal meetings, ask for an explanation). Obviously, a further assessment visit will be required (at significant extra cost), but depending on the situation found on the first visit and the policy of the assessors, the scope of this may be restricted to only those areas where the major problems were found. If the system was thought to be working well everywhere apart from the cutting and bending department, re-assessment may be restricted to this one problem department.

Whether there are only a few minor non-conformities (rarely are there none) and BS 5750 is awarded, or there is a major deficiency requiring re-assessment, the problems will, of course, be made quite clear. Not only will they be discussed with the management representative as they are identified, but a written statement will be prepared on what is effectively a corrective action form. These will be formally passed to the company and should then be dealt with in exactly the same way as internal corrective actions: an investigation is carried out, leading to a recommendation, followed by a management decision and, if appropriate, a change in the system. However, just as all internal corrective actions do not require a change in the system, the problems identified at the assessment might be a matter of applying the existing procedures better. Whatever the appropriate solution, the company will be expected to have taken effective steps to put matters right before the next visit by the assessors – whether this is a surveillance (following a successful first assessment) or a re-assessment.

AFTER PASSING BS 5750

Do not be discouraged. We have had to cover all the potential problems that may arise, but in fact the large majority of companies seeking BS 5750 pass at their first assessment. One reason for this is that if the internal quality system is followed, it should be apparent to a firm's management when the company is ready for assessment. If the quality system has not bedded-in sufficiently, there is little point going into an assessment in the hope that problems will disappear overnight or not be found on the day. A further point is that assessment firms would rather pass than fail you. Of course, they have to follow their own strict procedures and maintain the standards set by the NACCB, but every assessment body seeks to increase the list of firms they have successfully registered for BS 5750.

Whether or not you have passed BS 5750 will be clear by the end of the assessment; probably, the assessor will say so. However, there will be some delay until, with the assessor's own paperwork complete, it is official and the certificate is on your wall. The intervening period can be frustrating since, strictly speaking, you cannot yet claim to have BS 5750. You certainly must not say so in press releases or other publicity, still less use the BS 5750 mark. What can be done once it is official is discussed in the next chapter.

If all goes well, certainly open the champagne. The staff will more than deserve it. However, BS 5750 is not now over and done with. The quality system is ongoing and so is assessment. Some 6–12 months after the initial assessment the first regular surveillance visit will be made. Now the focus will be almost entirely on whether the quality system is still being followed (the initial assessment will have established that the system meets the requirements of the Standard). Normally, surveillance visits last a shorter time than the initial assessment visit and have a narrower scope. Any corrective actions raised as a result of the initial assessment may well be followed up, but in a shorter visit the operation of the system throughout the whole company cannot be covered and certain parts will be selected. In other respects, the surveillance visit will be carried out in exactly the same way as the initial assessment.

Surveillance visits will then be repeated at the intervals specified in the agreement with the assessors. After three years it is the policy of some assessors to repeat the whole cycle, starting with a full re-assessment. Other firms of assessors carry on with surveillance indefinitely. Whatever the practice, neglect in adherence to the quality system can result in BS 5750 registration being withdrawn. The negative impact of this could well exceed any initial benefits. The quality system must be kept up to scratch.

12   MARKETING BS 5750

This final chapter is about getting the best return from all the time and money spent on BS 5750. However, if you have a marketing department or regular advisers, they will undoubtedly be able to give better advice than can be covered in the few pages which follow.

We shall assume that the scope of registration for BS 5750 is the whole company. If, as is possible, only a part of the business has been covered, any marketing connected with BS 5750 must clearly relate only to the side of the business registered to BS 5750. The BS 5750 mark, for example, cannot be included on the company's letterhead if only one department has been assessed, although it may be possible to use it on a brochure which only relates to the department. The practical marketing problems raised by part-company registration, therefore, can be considerable and may be a good reason not to follow this route.

In the following pages we consider firstly, a marketing strategy for BS 5750, and then describe some of the tools which can be used to meet the strategic objectives.

A MARKETING STRATEGY

A suggested strategy is summarised in Figure 12.1.

Marketing activity can take place at various levels, each with a particular audience and appropriate tools. At all levels there should be a common message to communicate about the benefits conferred by BS 5750. This message can be stated in different ways, but should include the elements suggested below (although every communication does not have to cover the whole message).

Level	Objective	Audience	Tools
1	Awareness and image building	Customers, Potential Customers, Financial Supporters Suppliers The "Trade"	PR, Advertising Routine Communication
2	Stimulation of enquiries	Customers Potential Customers	As 1 plus: Direct mailing
3	Conversion of enquiries	Customers Potential Customers	As 1 and 2 plus: Quotation documents Brochures etc Face to face selling
4	Enhancement of customer satisfaction	Customers	Passing on internal benefits Customer satisfaction monitoring and complaint handling Customer mailing

Figure 12.1 Marketing BS 5750

- The Company is committed to quality.
- The Quality System in place both demonstrates that commitment and serves to enhance the quality of service offered.
- The Quality System has been assessed to meet the stringent requirements of BS 5750.
- Quality is no empty promise – the Company's observance of its own system is proven through the assessment.

Figure 12.2 The Marketing Message

At the first level, the objective is to create awareness and build the image of the company as a quality organisation. The primary audiences are customers and potential customers – in the longer run, through changing their perceptions, additional and perhaps more profitable business can be generated. However, there are others to influence as well including organisations which support the company financially, such as banks, suppliers (possibly to stimulate their quality of service to you) and the 'trade'. The latter includes competitors (for whatever reason, most companies want competitors to be impressed) and possibly even potential buyers of the company; BS 5750 may increase the value of the business when the time comes to sell.

The tools available at the first level include public relations (PR), advertising in its various forms, mailings and routine communication (eg inclusion of the BS 5750 mark on the letterhead).

The objective at the second level is more focused: to stimulate enquiries. The audience in this case is potential customers and existing customers who may currently not give you all the business they could. The tools are much as for the first level, but perhaps with more emphasis on focused methods such as direct marketing.

Improving the conversions of enquiries into orders is the objective at the third level. Nor is it just a matter of the crude ratio; what also matters is obtaining more profitable orders. BS 5750 may enable a firm to win orders from customers who, because of concerns about quality, might previously have placed only small, if any, orders. Also, a projection of the quality of the service offered may give opportunities to charge more; customers are often willing to pay more for what they perceive to be better. The tools used in pursuit of the first and second level objectives will all have a trickle-down effect on enquiry conversion (the potential customer stimulated to make an enquiry through a mailings already has a positive expectation of the service offered). More specific tools here include the quotation document which sets out the offer of a quality service, as well as other company literature which may be used in support. Also, and by no means least, the quality message must be reinforced in any face-to-face selling activity. The salesforce should be well briefed and know how to use BS 5750 in winning business.

The final level is the enhancement of customer satisfaction, which in turn leads back to enquiries and orders. The most important tool available is that a quality system implemented to meet BS 5750 will produce a higher quality of service to customers. It is performance, rather than promises, which convinces. However, supplementary marketing tools also include customer satisfaction monitoring (which should be built into the system) and, should things go wrong, complaint handling. Finally customers should be contacted routinely through such means as newsletters; BS 5750/quality is a powerful story with which to lead.

USE OF THE BS 5750 MARK

The right to use the BS 5750 mark of an accredited assessor is a very valuable. It has not been mentioned already simply because virtually all BS 5750-related activity will feature it.

The value of the mark might seem a trite thing. It is not. Unfortunately, as BS 5750 has increased in prominence and become a criterion for supplier selection, some companies have made doubtful, if not downright misleading, statements. Examples include:

> 'Working towards BS 5750.' (You can work towards something forever without either real effort or commitment)
> 'Quality to BS 5750 standards.' (Why not get BS 5750 then?)
> 'We recognise BS 5750 as an appropriate quality standard.' (Good for you!)

Things can be further fudged by playing around with letter size:

Working towards
BS 5750

Rightly or wrongly, such claims are made. However, unless its quality system has been successfully assessed by an accredited certification body, a company cannot use that assessor's BS 5750 mark. Since this is their mark, you can expect the assessors to pursue vigorously any who use it wrongfully.

Each assessor body has detailed rules governing the use of their own mark and you should read these and ask for clarification where there is any doubt; on surveillance visits, they check to make sure that the mark is not being misused. Most assessors have two versions of the mark available, ie with or without the crown or tick, as discussed in the previous chapter, and you can only use one or the other. However, assessment for BS 5750 also gives rights to use the equivalent ISO and EN Standards' mark and these may be used by certificate holders as well as, or even instead of, the BS 5750 mark. This right may be particularly important for an exporting company. Figure 12.3 illustrates one certification body's three versions of the mark.

Figure 12.3 International equivalents of the BS 5750 mark

Whatever the detailed rules, the BS 5750 mark (or the ISO or EN equivalents) can be used by registered companies in a wide variety of ways including:

- *Letterheads* The mark can be included on company stationery.
- *Company literature* As long as it is not implied any specific product is covered by BS 5750, the mark can be used in most literature and brochures.
- *Media advertising* Media adverts can also carry the mark subject to the restriction on product links.
- *Vehicles* BS 5750 can be shown on the delivery fleet or other vehicles.

- *Buildings* Flags and other methods can be used to display the mark in or near the company's premises.

While the mark can be used in any of these ways, you can be selective. For various reasons it may be thought inappropriate, for example, to include it on the letterhead.

The one place you cannot use the BS 5750 mark is on your products or their packaging and by extension you must not suggest in other ways that a product meets BS 5750. The logic here is quite unassailable: BS 5750 is a standard for quality management; it is not a product standard. A BS 5750 company is clearly committed to quality, but as such, registration to the Standard implies nothing about the product specification or method of manufacture. Where a physical product is produced, there should be no ambiguity about the prohibition on relating BS 5750 to the product. In some service companies, however, the matter may be less than clear-cut. If in any doubt, discuss the matter with your assessors.

A final comment on the use of the BS 5750 mark. If you do not keep the quality system up to scratch and eventually lose registration, you may no longer use it. Removal of the mark from literature, vehicles and the building could be very expensive – another reason to make sure you keep your registration.

PUBLIC RELATIONS

Your BS 5750 can be just sent through the post. A more formal presentation, however, is an event on which to hang a press release. The person making the presentation can be almost anybody, including the chairman's wife, but the better known they are the greater the impact of the story. Some presenters to consider include:

- A representative of the assessor firm.
- A 'name' in your own industry – the chairman of the trade association etc.
- Someone senior from a major customer or a large company in the market you supply.
- A local worthy – the mayor, etc. This type of presentation is most appropriate if your market is mainly local.
- Someone nationally known, eg a major politician – not out of the question if you can persuade him that the story will benefit him, too. Politicians are seldom shy of positive publicity.

The actual presentation does not have to be a formal affair; just a photo-call will do, unless you want to make it an event for the staff as well. Please do not skimp on the photography – half a dozen snaps with a cheap camera will be no use. Bring in a professional.

A story needs preparing for the press release. This should not be over-long; a page or two at the most is enough, with possibly versions tailored to fit the interests of different publications. The content of the story depends on the company and its business but themes will probably include:

- The company's business and (very briefly) its history.
- Why BS 5750 was sought.
- How it was obtained. (You should convey all the hard work and commitment, but it is perhaps better to suggest that many of the quality procedures were already in place in some form.)
- What BS 5750 means for customers – this is the most important angle of all.

If your company is a 'BS 5750 first' in your industry, this also should be featured and may enable you to obtain specially good coverage.

Target media for the press releases include: the trade press of your business (you ought to get a mention here), the trade press of the major markets you supply and the local press. Send each a copy of the story, preferably tailored to their specific interests (eg a local flavour for the local press), together with a good quality and labelled (naming who is who) photograph. You can, of course, try the national press, but unless you have a really special story and hire professional PR help as well, your chances are very slim.

As well as the presentation, other PR opportunities are available. One is to follow up in the trade press by offering articles on the benefits of BS 5750 to the industry or how your company went about getting the registration. If you do not feel your in-house writing talents are up to the task, you can buy-in a ghost writer cheaply. A 'letters to the editor' section in the trade press is another opportunity.

If you regularly issue press releases, you should consider tagging a BS 5750 angle on to other stories. In a press release about winning a major order, for example, you can mention BS 5750 registration and perhaps imply a connection with the new business.

PR activity can be wider than press releases. Almost anything that gets your name across 'free' can be considered. Articles on BS 5750 can be followed up with taking part in seminars and conferences. There are also events like customer days to consider.

Publicity Material

Virtually all firms have some existing publicity material and this should be changed to feature BS 5750. Just to include the BS 5750 mark is not really enough – not all recipients of the material will fully understand what it means and a least a paragraph on the quality policy and what this offers customers should be included. The expense of the design work and reprinting, however, may be considerable and you may wish to phase in the new edition as the old stocks run out. Alternatively, you might see the need to include a BS 5750 reference as a good opportunity to replace old and tired material.

If your company regularly advertises in the trade or other press, you should probably change the advertisement copy to include the BS 5750 mark. You might also consider special ads at the time you gain the Standard or change the long-term focus of your advertising to feature quality of service. If your original advertising copy was professionally designed, do not just stick the BS 5750 mark in the only blank space available; have it re-designed properly. If your advertising copy was not designed professionally in the first place, now is a good opportunity to upgrade.

As well as adapting existing literature, you could consider having some BS 5750-specific material. This might be used for a special 'launch' mail-out to your existing and potential customers. One suggestion here is to use your quality policy. This can be printed attractively and include the BS 5750 mark. You might also consider either a special edition of your company newsletter or, if you do not have one, producing a 'one-off'. This can cover how and why you sought BS 5750, give an outline of the quality system and what it offers customers. Even a simple letter to customers is far better than nothing; you cannot expect more business to come from BS 5750 if nobody knows you have got it.

As mentioned earlier, the quality manual (not the procedure manual) can also be regarded as promotional material, although it is better used selectively to meet a specific request or perhaps sent to a few major customers. It is not just a matter of the expense of reproducing it. Frankly, recipients will find the average manual a bit on the dull side. Again, produce it to a good standard, although this might well be possible in-house.

One other important document to consider is the quotation. This can take various forms, depending on the nature of your business, from a one-page letter up to a lengthy proposal document. It should, in all cases, be seen as a selling document, not just as a contract offer. Customers should be given reasons to buy from your firm. BS 5750 should, therefore, be mentioned in the quotation. Certainly include the mark, but as well say something about your quality system, what BS 5750 registration means and the benefits offered to customers.

Customer Satisfaction Monitoring

Customer satisfaction monitoring and complaint handing will be built into your quality system to provide an external measure of whether you are meeting requirements. However, the contact with customers entailed should also be seen as a marketing opportunity. Sending off a short satisfaction questionnaire is another opportunity to keep in touch with customers, perhaps with a follow-up letter to any comments they make. This demonstrates that you value customer care and interaction. However, monitoring does not have to be only postal. Key customers, at least, can be followed up personally by a senior manager, who can use the need for quality system monitoring as a reason for making contact.

Even with an effective quality system in-place, some customers will complain. This will of course trigger some quality system procedures, including an investigation to find a long-term solution to the problem. However, the fact that such a complaint is taken so seriously should be turned to a marketing advantage with the particular customer left believing that, whilst an error occurred, everything possible was done to put the matter right and prevent a recurrence.

The Salesforce

In many businesses the salesforce is the major source of both enquiry generation and order conversion, with business dependent on their face-to-face selling skills. It is important, therefore, that they are trained to tell customers the BS 5750 story. How this is done needs careful thought, with time set aside to make sure they are adequately briefed. This should cover the use of publicity material to reinforce the quality message.

A FINAL WORD

BS 5750 can offer enormous marketing opportunities. However, it can also be a cross to bear: you have to live up to your commitment to quality. Promises are a start in any business dealings, but they soon become very thin if performance does not match up. It is all very well, therefore, telling customers that your BS 5750 registration offers an enhanced quality service; they must experience it as well. In the long term the quality system must be used to produce continual quality improvement. Marketing activity can then communicate what has actually been achieved. Only in the very short term can marketing be an alternative to real service. Despite what you tell them, customers will learn that what you do is not what you say.

Quality also has to extend to the marketing activity itself. It is, for example, false economy to mail out the quality policy in the form of a tatty photocopy. Also make sure your marketing reflects that attention to detail which has to be built into a quality system. One of the authors of this book organised a mail-out of a letter with a copy of the quality policy included, as soon as BS 5750 was gained. One recipient took delight in pointing out that his envelope contained the letter, but not the quality policy. Perhaps a review of the mail-out procedures was required . . .

Appendix 1
BS 5750 Schemes For Stockists

On the whole, this book has been aimed at companies involved in producing a product or service. For this sort of company, BS 5750 Parts 1, 2, or 3 (or the equivalent ISO standards) apply to their activities. In many respects, the requirements of the Standard can be easily fitted to most of the operations of such companies.

However, when we are dealing with companies involved in various forms of stockholding, the normal application of BS 5750 is more difficult to achieve. For this reason separate schemes have been developed: *The Registered Stockist Scheme* from BSI Quality Assurance and *The National Stockist Scheme* from other assessment bodies. 'Stockist' includes distributors, wholesalers and retailers.

The stockist schemes cover an important step in the cascade of goods from manufacturers to ultimate customer (we are invariably talking about manufactured products rather than services). Many manufacturers produce goods in large quantities for ultimate customers who typically require them in relatively small quantities. In such cases, it is often inappropriate for the manufacturers to deal directly with customers and so the link is made via a stockist. Stockists take in goods from manufacturers (often, but not always, in large quantities) and sell them on in small quantities. Frequently such stockists will specialise in a particular type of product (eg metal fastenings, axial fans etc) in which case they may buy products from several different manufacturers.

How in such cases can the customer be sure that he is actually buying materials from a BS 5750-registered manufacturing source? In the same way, how can a BS 5750 manufacturer be sure that his product is actually reaching the customer without being mixed up with products from non-approved companies? By becoming a member of a stockist scheme, a stockist undertakes to ensure that this important link is made, enabling BS 5750 quality-assured products to maintain their distinct identity from original manufacturer through to ultimate customer.

The means by which this is achieved is, in fact, a derivative of BS 5750 Part 2. By applying the various elements of this Standard to the stockist situation, most assessment companies have created a specification to enable a stockist to register to BS 5750. These involve developing certain key elements of the stockholding activity and defining how the requirements of the standard should be applied to them. For example:

- **Purchasing** This lays great emphasis on the Stockist buying from BS 5750 assured companies. If for any reason goods are purchased from non-approved sources then the stockist must make this fact clear in writing, to their customers.
- **Process Control** This deals with the methods used in controlling all aspects of the stock (quantities, storage conditions, stock rotation, record keeping, etc).
- **Product Identification And Traceability** Here (in the Registered Stockist scheme of BSI Quality Assurance) the stockist chooses one of two schemes, either Level A (for material requiring 'source lot traceability') or Level B (where such traceability is not required). In this context 'source lot traceability' means being able to track the product in question (or the lot or batch of products) back into the manufacturing company and to the original records made at the time of manufacture. Certain industries buying components through stockists require such traceability to enable products to be recalled if a fault is found within a batch or production run after their final product has left the company. Level B does not require traceability to this degree, but does require that products can be traced back to the source of supply – but not to a particular batch, etc. Stockist schemes of other assessors do not make a distinction comparable to BSI's Levels A and B.

Many of the other areas of the Standard apply in precisely the same way as for any other company. For example, Management Review, Corrective Action and Internal Quality Audit require the same degree of attention in a stockist as in a manufacturing or service company.

The task of the stockist, then, is to produce a documented quality system, in the same way as described elsewhere in this book for manufacturing or service companies. This system must meet the requirements of BS 5750 Part 2 interpreted for the stockist's situation. Most assessment companies will provide details of their own schemes for becoming registered. This will almost certainly include their own specification for the application of BS 5750 to the stockist situation. Once the documented quality system has been created and successfully implemented, the assessment process continues in the identical way described in chapter 11.

There remains one area which can, and frequently does, cause difficulties for stockist companies. Most stockists will be solely involved in the supply of goods or materials which have not been significantly changed from their original manufactured shape. However, some companies may offer a service involving limited adjustment to the product. For example, an electrical wholesaler may buy cable in 100m lengths and offer shorter lengths to customers. This can be regarded as normal stockholding activity; confusingly, it will be classified within the Stockist Scheme as 'repackaging'. The difficulties lie in how far down this road a stockist can go before 'repackaging' becomes 'processing' and therefore outside the scope of the Stockist Scheme. It is surprising how many companies who would consider themselves as stockists are actually involved in other activities (product adjustment, repairs, modifications etc) which move them in the direction of a 'normal' (ie, non-Stockist) Part 2 application. If in any doubt, it is advisable to select the assessment company earlier than normal in the project and to prepare the quality system in the light of their advice.

Appendix 2
SOME USEFUL CONTACTS

DTI

The DTI operates through regional offices which are listed in local phone books. There is also a central enquiry point. Tel: 071-215 5000

DTI Enterprise Initiative Contractors

Salford University Business Services Ltd
Technology House
Salford University Business Park
Lissadel Street
Salford M6 6AP
Tel: 061-736 2843
Fax: 061-737 7700

Pera International
Nottingham Road
Melton Mowbray
Leicestershire
LE13 0PB
Tel: 0664 501501
Fax: 0664 501264

Consultancy Associations

Association of Quality Management Consultants (AQMC)
4 Beyne Road
Olivers Battery
Winchester
Hants. SO22 4JW
Tel: 0962 864394
Fax: 0962 866969

Management Consultancies Association Ltd
11 West Halkin Street
London SW1X 8JL
Tel: 071-235 3897
Fax: 071-235 0825

Appendix 3
ACCREDITED CERTIFICATION BODIES FOR BS 5750

Associated Offices Quality Certification Ltd
Longridge House
Longridge Place
Manchester M60 4DT
Tel: 061-833 2295
Fax: 061-833 9965

ASTA Certification Services
Prudential Chambers
23/24 Market Place
Rugby CV21 3DU
Tel: 0788 578435
Fax: 0788 573605

BSI Quality Assurance
PO Box 375
Milton Keynes
MK14 6LL
Tel: 0908 220908
Fax: 0908 220671

British Approvals Service for Electric Cables
Silbury Court
360 Silbury Boulevard
Milton Keynes
MK9 2AF
Tel: 0908 691121
Fax: 0908 692722

Bureau Veritas Quality International Ltd
3rd Floor
70 Borough High Street
London SE1 1XF
Tel: 071-378 8113
Fax: 071-378 8014

Central Certification Service Ltd
Victoria House
123 Midland Road
Wellingborough
Northants NN8 1LU
Tel: 0933 441796
Fax: 0933 440247

Ceramic Industry Certification Scheme Ltd
Queens Road
Penkhull
Stoke-on-Trent ST4 7LQ
Tel: 0782 411008
Fax: 0782 412331

Construction Quality Assurance Ltd
Arcade Chambers
The Arcade, Market Place
Howark, Notts NG24 1UD
Tel: 0636 708700
Fax: 0636 708766

Det Norske Veritas Quality Assurance Ltd
Veritas House
112 Station Road
Sidcup, Kent DA15 7RU
Tel: 081-309 7477
Fax: 081-309 5907

Electrical Equipment Certification
Service
Health & Safety Executive
Harpur Hill
Buxton
Derbyshire SK17 9JN
Tel: 0298 26211
Fax: 0298 79514

Engineering Inspection Authorities
Board
c/o Institution of Mechanical Engineers
1 Birdcage Walk
London SW1H 9JJ
Tel: 071-973 1271
Fax: 071-222 4557

Lloyd's Register Quality Assurance Ltd
Norfolk House
Wellesley Road
Croydon
CR9 2DT
Tel: 081-688 6882/3
Fax: 081-681 8146

National Approval Council for Security
Systems
Queensgate House
14 Cookham Road
Maidenhead
Berkshire SL6 8AJ
Tel: 0628 37512
Fax: 0628 773367

National Quality Assurance Ltd
5 Cotswold Business Park
Millfield Lane
Caddington, Beds LU1 4AR
Tel: 0582 841144
Fax: 0582 841288

SIRA Certification Service
Saighton Lane
Saighton
Chester
CH3 6EG
Tel: 0244 332200
Fax: 0244 332112

SGS Yarsley Quality Assured Firms Ltd
Trowers Way
Redhill
Surrey
RH1 2JN
Tel: 0737 768445
Fax: 0737 761229

The Loss Prevention Certification Board
Ltd
Malrose Avenue
Boreham Wood
Hertfordshire
WD6 2BJ
Tel: 081-207 2345
Fax: 081-207 6305

The Quality Scheme for Ready Mixed
Concrete
3 High Street
Hampton
Middlesex
TW12 2SQ
Tel: 081-941 0273
Fax: 081-979 4558

TRADA QA Services Ltd
Stocking Lane
Hughenden Valley
High Wycombe
Bucks HP14 4NR
Tel: 0494 565484
Fax: 0494 564587

UK Certificating Authority for
Reinforcing Steels
Oak House
Tubs Hill
Sevenoaks
Kent TN13 1RL
Tel: 0732 450000
Fax: 0732 455917

Source: NACCB, June 1992

Index